Lectures on Mathematics in the Life Sciences

# SOME MATHEMATICAL
# QUESTIONS IN BIOLOGY. II

The American Mathematical Society
Providence, Rhode Island
1972

**Proceedings of the Fourth Symposium on
Mathematical Biology held in Boston, December, 1969.**

**edited by
Jack D. Cowan**

International Standard Book Number 0-8218-1153-3
AMS 1970 Subject Classification 92A05

Prepared by the American Mathematical Society
with the support of the Institute of Defense Analyses

Printed in the United States of America
Copyright © by the American Mathematical Society

# CONTENTS

## FOREWORD

This volume contains lectures given at the Fourth Symposium on Some Mathematical Questions in Biology, held in Boston on December 27, 1969, in conjunction with the annual meeting of the American Association for the Advancement of Science. The purpose of this series of symposia, which are co-sponsored by the American Mathematical Society and the Society for Industrial and Applied Mathematics, is to stimulate a closer relationship between mathematicians, and biologists with some mathematical background.

The lectures in this volume are concerned with some of the most interesting and basic problems of contemporary biology: the molecular and cellular control of differentiation and development in multicellular organisms. The spectacular development of molecular biology over the past two decades has led many biologists to suppose that almost every aspect of cellular and multicellular organization can be elucidated in molecular terms only, that all the necessary information resides in the genes, and that if only the genetic message can be deciphered, then organisms can be reconstructed, at least in principle. This fallacy has turned up in a modified form in contemporary brain research, where molecular explanations for learning and memory are vigorously propounded. In fact, although it is undoubtedly true that genetic information is necessary for the reconstruction of the organism, it is not sufficient. Information of any kind does not exist by itself as an independent entity, but is a process which an observer can report as being present in the interaction between two or more systems. Messages have to be decoded and interpreted in specific ways if information flow can be said to take place. Thus cells must contain transcription and decoding machinery of a complicated character for the transmission of genetic messages. By the same token there must exist in multicellular organisms, mechanisms both for the generation of specific patterns of cellular activities, and for their interpretation in multicellular terms by way of cellular interactions, otherwise it is difficult to see how such systems could be organised. Although it is the case that such activities and interactions must ultimately be explicable in terms of specific molecular processes, it is by no means clear that an understanding of the larger scale organization can be couched in only molecular terms. The details would obscure the overall pattern.

This is the view of many developmental biologists, who see organisms not in terms of molecules switching on and off in a static computer-like fashion, but in terms of ubiquitous activities and incessant processes. It is in such an area that theoretical biology and biomathematics is beginning to flourish. Indeed it was a distinguished mathematician, A. M. Turing, who in 1952 published the first detailed theory of morphogenesis,[1] based on the supposed ability of cells to respond to concentration gradients of diffusing chemical substances produced somewhere in the field of cells comprising the embryo. This theory lay fallow until very recently when L. Wolpert,[2] B. C. Goodwin and M. H. Cohen,[3] F. H. C. Crick,[4] I. Prigogine[5] and others took up once again the question of morphogenesis and differentiation. The lectures by M. H. Cohen and B. C. Goodwin, the creators of the first real alternative to the Turing theory, are concerned with both theoretical and experimental aspects of this topic. The third lecture in this volume by S. Kauffman is concerned to bridge the gap between what is known about genetic control mechanisms at the molecular level, i.e., the Jacob-Monod theory of repressor and inducer genes,[6] and the overall dynamics of cellular activities.

I believe that these lectures clearly demonstrate the emergence of a new facet of biology: the theoretical biology of development. Simple mathematical ideas are very much involved in this aspect of biology, as they are in many other aspects of the life sciences.

It is a pleasure to acknowledge the support provided by the Institute for Defense Analyses.

Jack D. Cowan
Department of Theoretical Biology
University of Chicago
November 22, 1971

[1] A. M. Turing, Phil. Trans. Roy. Soc. **B**, **237**, (1952), 37.

[2] L. Wolpert, J. Theor. Biol. **25**, (1969), 1-47.

[3] B. C. Goodwin and M. H. Cohen, J. Theor. Biol. **25** (1969), 49-107.

[4] F. H. C. Crick, Nature **225** (1970), 420-422.

[5] I. Prigogine, Proc. Second International Conference on Theoretical Physics and Biology, Institut de la Vie, Versailles, 1969.

[6] F. Jacob and J. Monod, Cold Spring Harbor Sympos. Quantitative Biology, vol. 22, 1961, p. 163.

# MODELS OF CLOCKS AND MAPS IN DEVELOPING ORGANISMS*

By

## MORREL H. COHEN

*The University of Chicago*

*Supported in part by the Office of Naval Research and the Alfred P. Sloan Foundation.

## Abstract

We begin with a brief description of the major events in the development of a multicellular organism to its adult or culminating stage. Some of the basic concepts which have emerged thus far in developmental biology are listed. It is argued that certain of the basic problems of the control of development can be reduced to the construction of clocks or maps. Control by a stationary process such as diffusion or active transport of a control substance is described as a model for the establishment of a map, i.e., of Wolpert's positional information. Control by periodic events allows in addition for the existence of clocks. Such a periodic event in one cell which can trigger the corresponding event in a neighboring cell propagates as an organizing wave. These are described in some detail. Two examples of how positional information can be set up by organizing waves are given, one being a new single-event model and the other being the two-event model of Goodwin and Cohen. It is pointed out that models based on periodic events need not necessarily involve propagation, a phase diffusion model being given as an example and Physarum polycephalum discussed in some detail in relation to it.

## 1. Introduction

Most complex organisms start their existence as fertilized eggs. The transition from egg to adult is *development*. Many cells are derived from the initial cell by *cell division* or *cleavage*. Various cell types are then generated from the early cells by *differentiation*. The cells are organized: form develops by *morphogenesis* and in-

3

ternal structure by *pattern formation*. The organization proceeds by cleavage and division, by movement, and by progressive specialization via differentiation. The processes are quite precisely controlled. They are controlled temporally, i.e., they occur in an orderly sequence, and controlled spatially, i.e., they occur in characteristic positions with the temporal sequences in different positions correlated. Watching time-lapse films of a developing organism is a remarkable experience. The spatial and temporal control is dramatically evident. It is as though each cell has access to a clock and a map. (I use "map" here in the same sense in which Wolpert [1] uses "positional information".) In the present paper, I review selectively the existing attempts to construct models of clocks and maps with some emphasis on the work of Goodwin and myself [2] and introduce several new ideas as well. My purposes in doing so are first to help in establishing an arsenal of theoretical weapons which would then be available for the quantitative analysis of the development of particular organisms, e. g. as is presently being carried out by Robertson and myself for the cellular slime molds [3], [4], and second to put the theoretical problems of the control of development in a proper biological context for more mathematical readers.

Such models must be internally consistent, consistent with the known biological facts and plausible in relation to them, quantifiable, predictive, and testable. We must therefore restrict our studies to the total development of very simple organisms (e.g. the cellular slime molds) (Bonner [5]), to the early embryo of more complex organisms (e. g. the sea urchin) (Gustafson and Wolpert [6]), or to the development of particular organ systems of still more complex organisms (e. g. the retinal-tectal projection) (Gaze, Keating, Szekely and Beazley [7]).

The models we are to describe must, in addition, make contact with established embryological knowledge, much of which has been organized around a series of key concepts (Balinsky [8]; Huxley and de Beer [9]). I describe some of these briefly here. The cells within the embryo of a simple organism, the early embryo of a complex organism, or a single tissue of a later embryo form a *field* (Child [10]) in the sense that they are functionally coupled to each other and not to cells outside the field. This functional coupling is probably quite generally associated with specialized junctions between cells in contact having low electrical resistivity (Furshpan and Potter [11]). Each field has a definite *polarity*, a distinction between "up" and "down". Associated with the polarity there are *gradients* of cellular activity, character, or potential character [10]. Associated with such a gradient there will be an *axis* which is normally an axis of symmetry of the embryo or tissue. There will be an *organizing center* normally located at the pole of the axis, which plays a dominant role in subsequent determination of evolving pattern (Spemann [12]). Embryonic patterns are frequently size invariant over a broad range, i.e., embryos *regulate* [8], [9]. This in turn implies that cells within a field are *competent* to differentiate into a larger set of cell types than is normally required [8], [9]. Suppose that we make an abstract characterization of the state of an individual cell by specification of all variables relevant to development. We could then represent each cell state as a point in an abstract cell-state space. The point associated with a given cell would trace out a path in that space as development proceeds. Cell types would correspond to stable points or cycles in that space. Our present concern would be with the initiation, control, and coordination of the paths followed by the cells of a field.

## 2. Quasistatic control

In more explicitly biological terms, the existence of a map or positional information would imply that cell state varies with position over a field. The variation of cell state, however, is far subtler than that involved in differentiation, which implies change of cell type. The positional information is first established, then the pattern of differentiation proceeds to develop by *interpretation*, in Wolpert's phrase [1], of the positional information. The development is controlled by the variations in cell state which comprise the map. These can be dynamical or quasistatic in character. We begin by discussing examples of the latter because of their greater simplicity.

The simplest possible model of a map is that there is a gradient of the concentration of a substance, a morphogen, present in the field $c = c(x)$ where $x$ is measured along an appropriate developmental axis. Crick [13] has pointed out that Wolpert's estimate that fields are 50–100 cells in linear dimension [1] implies that there is ample time for the establishment by diffusion of a concentration gradient during development. Once the gradient is set up, development proceeds by morphogenetic movements or by differentiation according to the particular value of $c$ in each part of the field. The difficulty is how the gradient is set up and maintained thereafter.

One very simple model posits a set of source cells which maintain the concentration of the morphogen at $c_1$ at one end of the developmental axis and another set of sink cells which maintain the concentration at $c_0 < c_1$ at the other end of the axis. The axis itself is the path of steepest descent of the concentration from $c_1$ to $c_0$. The source cells generate the morphogen, which diffuses passively through the field to the sink cells where it is destroyed. The pattern of concentration satisfies Laplace's equation (ignoring finite cell size) subject to the boundary conditions of negligible loss at the borders of the field and the presence of the source and sink.

$$(2.1) \qquad \nabla^2 c = 0, \qquad \nabla c \cdot \hat{n} = 0,$$

where $\hat{n}$ is the unit normal to the boundary.

The big difficulty with the simple diffusion model is that it has to be augmented rather awkwardly to fit various cutting and transplanting experiments with embryos which regulate. Suppose a segment is excised from the above field. The maximum concentration in it will be less than $c_1$ and the minimum greater than $c_0$. Moreover, the boundary cells are neither source nor sink cells. For regulation to occur, i.e., for the same concentration pattern to occur scaled down to the new size, the boundary cells must evolve towards source or sink cells. This requires that cells sense that they are at the edge of a field and differentiate into source or sink cells accordingly. Thus, to make the diffusion model work, one requires predifferentiated source and sink cells and a regulation mechanism entirely outside the diffusion model itself. It therefore seems unlikely to me that the simple diffusion model will be found in a regulating embryo. Moreover, for those fields which develop real complexity of pattern, it seems unlikely that control via variation of morphogen concentration is sufficient. Instead, one expects to find the diffusion mechanisms operant in the least demanding of situations, as for aggregation of the simplest of the cellular slime molds (Bonner [5]).

Lawrence has observed certain anomalous bristle patterns on milkweed bugs and has artifically produced similar patterns via his sand-hill model [14].

He has suggested that active transport may underly his sand-hill model. I feel that active transport may offer a more promising basis for map generation than simple diffusion, quite generally. For example, I have developed the following regulating model based on active transport. The total current density $j$ of morphogen within the field consists of two parts, a diffusion current $j_D$ and an active transport current $j_A$:

$$(2.2) \qquad j = j_D + j_A.$$

The diffusion current is proportional to the local concentration gradient in the usual way,

$$(2.3) \qquad j_D = - D\nabla c,$$

but the diffusion coefficient $D$ contains contributions from inter- as well as intra-cellular diffusion. The active transport current $j_A$ is produced by the pumping of each cell against the local concentration gradient. In the particular case that each cell is polar, there can be a preferred axis in the field along which a current can flow in the absence of the gradient. As the concentration gradient increases, the active transport process presumably becomes less and less effective in pumping uphill and $j_A$ decreases towards zero. One simple form for $j_A$ in those circumstances would be

$$(2.4) \qquad j_A = j_0 \hat{a}/1 + (\hat{a} \cdot \nabla c/c_m')^2.$$

Thus for small concentration gradients along the polar axis ($\hat{a}$ is a unit vector parallel to the axis of polarity), the current $j_0$ flows in the direction $\hat{a}$. When $\hat{a} \cdot \nabla c$, the component of the concentration gradient in the direction of active transport significantly exceeds the characteristic value $c_m'$, active transport effectively ceases.

We now suppose that the active transport mechanism and the intercellular diffusion are linked to the existence of specialized junctions between cells within a field.

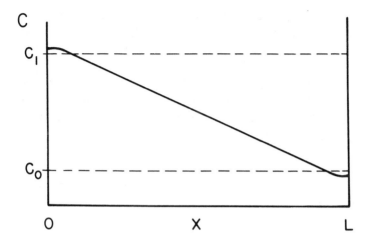

FIGURE 1. Morphogen concentration $c$ as a function of position $x$ in an embryonic field in which the morphogen is actively transported to the left. When the concentration exceeds $c_1$, the morphogen is destroyed. When it falls below $c_0$, the morphogen is generated. There results a regulating map.

We therefore expect that leakage of the morphogen by diffusion through the cell membranes on the exterior boundaries of the field may be neglected, i.e., that the normal component of $j$ vanishes over the boundaries of the field.

To complete the model we suppose that, apart from active transport, any cell in the field is in a state of neutral equilibrium in relation to its internal morphogen concentration $c$ provided $c_0 < c < c_1$. When $c < c_0$, on the other hand, a cell generates morphogen, and when $c > c_1$ a cell destroys it.

The stable, steady-state solution for the position dependence of $c$ is sketched for the one-dimensional case in Figure 1. There is a region of concentration above $c_1$ at the positive pole of the axis and one below $c_0$ at the negative pole. The extent of these regions is small if the rates of generation and destruction are sufficiently large. There results the regulating solution

$$(2.5) \qquad c(x) \cong c_1 - (c_1 - c_0)(x/L),$$

in which concentration depends only on position $x$ measured relative to the length $L$ of the field along its axis.

No active transport mechanism specific to the setting up of positional information has yet been identified in embryonic tissues. Nevertheless, there are attractive features to such active transport models of maps as the above example which lead me to take them seriously. The active transport, generation, and destruction of the morphogen can occur in any cell of the field. All cells are equicompetent with regard to map generation. All processes are metabolically based. Wolpert has stressed the importance of a metabolic basis for, e.g., polarity [1]. Finally, it is not a trivial matter to construct models of maps based on intercellular interaction which are size invariant, i.e., regulate.

## 3. Organizing waves

In the last section we gave two examples of the control of development via a quasistatic process, simple diffusion and active transport. In these models, different regions of the field are launched along their separate paths of development according to their local values of morphogen concentration $c$. There is no further coordination of the differing courses of development in the different regions, which is a serious weakness in these models. Also, as mentioned earlier, it seems unlikely that great spatial specificity, as in, e.g., the nervous system, or complexity of pattern can emerge by interpretation of a simple pattern of morphogen concentration.

The simplest and most reliable method of establishing temporal organization over an entire field is by use of a clock. All known clocks are based either on periodic events or steady rate processes. I focus here on clocks based on periodicity as more appropriate for biological systems. Goodwin and Cohen [2] have introduced on elaborate model for the control of development which is based on periodic biochemical events. (I shall refer to their paper as [2] hereafter.) I now give an account of the ideas in [2] relevant to the present broader exposition of models for the control of development and with a somewhat different presentation and emphasis from the original.

Suppose there to be in each cell in a field a periodic event (the $S$-event) which might be quite complex in character but which has at least one simple aspect, the signalling aspect. Let the period of the $S$-event be $T$, and let the concentration of some signalling substance have a time course brief relative to $T$ (the signalling aspect) as shown in Figure 13 of [2]. The period $T$ must be short on the developmental time scale for the $S$-event to be useful as a clock. $T$ also must be long compared to molecular generation times for there to be a number of different time slots within a period during which different and specific molecules can be made. Since the former times are of order hours and the latter of order seconds, $T$ must be of order minutes.

At this point, Goodwin and Cohen (GC) call attention to the existence of tight junctions and low membrane resistivity as a basis for functional coupling between cells within a field. They suppose, in particular, that the $S$-event in one cell can control the $S$-event in a neighboring cell because of this functional coupling. They suppose there to be three relevant cell states:

(i) Off and sensitive. This state occurs before the signalling aspect of the $S$-event. During this state a cell can be signalled by a nearest neighbor which is itself passing through the signalling aspect. When a cell is signalled during the sensitive period, its entire cycle is phase shifted so that the signalling aspect occurs after a time delay $\Delta t_s$ following reception of the signal.

(ii) On and signalling. During this state, the cell is producing the signalling substance $\Sigma$ which, via functional coupling with the cell's nearest neighbors, causes them to go "on" after the time delay $\Delta t_s$.

(iii) Off and insensitive. This state lasts for the refractory period

$$(3.1) \qquad\qquad T_r = rT,$$

during which reception of a signal from a nearest neighbor evokes no response. There is no shifting of the phase of the periodic $S$-event by a signal received during this portion of the cycle.

These three states are idealized in Figure 2.

GC show that provided there are certain initial phase and frequency relations among all the cells in the field, waves, termed organizing waves, propagate *outward* from a region of cells, termed the pacemaker, in pulsatile fashion. These waves do not possess a superposition principle, but do admit a Huyghens construction and satisfy an eikonal equation. The boundary conditions are absorbing for waves propagating into the boundary because of the refractory period, and secondary sources occur at the edges of waves propagating away from the boundary so that wave fronts either are closed or terminate on boundaries. The propagation velocity is

$$(3.2) \qquad\qquad v_s = \xi d / \Delta t,$$

where $d$ is a mean cell diameter and $\xi$ is a geometric

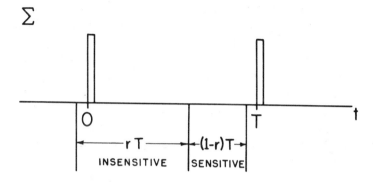

FIGURE 2. Schematic rendering of the time course of the state of a cell in relation to the $S$-event. The concentration of the signalling agent $\Sigma$ is idealized as a square wave.

correction factor perhaps 10% less than unity. The reader is referred to [2] for further details.

The organizing waves propagate outward from the pacemaker region and sweep through the entire field (or tissue to use less specialized language). Because of the existence of a refractory period, the initial phase relations of the autonomous $S$ oscillations of every cell have to be such that each cell is sensitive when signalled by its neighbors. Otherwise propagation of the wave would be blocked locally. Moreover, each cell must be sufficiently well into its sensitive period that fluctuations in $T, r,$ and $\Delta t_s$ do not lead to any appreciable change of the signal during the refractory period. That is, the system must be stable against internally generated noise. GC solve this problem by observing that every embryo starts out from one cell, the egg. The $S$-event must have a metabolic basis; it is reasonable to suppose that the $S$-event starts recurring periodically either immediately after the egg is fertilized or during the period of the early, synchronous cleavages. However, as the $S$-event persists after cell division stops, it is clearly independent of the cell-division cycle. In this way, the cells are initially in synchrony or close to it, which guarantees continued, stable propagation of the organizing waves.

Clearly, the pacemaker region will contain those cells having the highest autonomous frequencies. These will automatically entrain their slower neighbors by triggering them before they would have reached their signalling aspect on their own. The entire geometry of the set of organizing wavefronts depends on the location of the pacemaker region within the tissue. Reproducible embryonic patterns will occur only if the pacemaker is reproducibly located. This in turn requires a frequency gradient in the tissue which ultimately can be traced back to a frequency gradient in the early embryo, after the first set of cell divisions is completed. Metabolic gradients are known to exist at that stage (Child [10]). Ultimately, however, one must recognize that the asymmetry of the frequency distribution originates either in an initial asymmetry in the egg or because of a special mechanism which sets up and maintains the frequency gradient, an example of which will be given later.

The organizing waves originate at the pacemaker at a well-defined location in the field and propagate outward from it. There is a family of orthogonal trajectories of rays emanating from the pacemaker region. The organizing waves terminate at the end of the longest orthogonal trajectory. Organizing wave propagation thus has many of the features required of a control system by experimental embryology. The pacemaker clearly corresponds to the organizer of classical embryology, the maximal orthogonal trajectory to the axis of development, the direction of propagation of the organizing waves along the axis to polarity, and in addition there is a frequency gradient and a phase gradient along the axis.

However, despite these correspondences, propagation of a single organizing wave does not establish a complete control system for development. One may regard the periodic $S$-event of each cell as its local development clock. The $S$-wave causes all the local clocks to be entrained by the pacemaker, ensuring that there is a single clock for the entire field which operates at the frequency of the pacemaker. Although the phase of the $S$-event varies with position in the field, this does not by itself constitute positional information because there is no real change in cell state with position. There is no map contained within the model as it is presently constructed. In order to introduce positional information, we must introduce a controlled change in cell state with position. A very natural way of doing so is by establishing a varying phase difference between two related periodic events within a single cell. I discuss two ways of doing this in the present paper, a new model in the next section, and the phase-shift model of Goodwin and Cohen in §5.

## 4. The single-event model

The most economical way to set up a map based on organizing waves is via what I shall call the single-event model. For simplicity, I shall consider a line of $N + 1$ cells, numbered consecutively from 0 to $N$ with 0 the pacemaker. I suppose there to be a linear dependence of autonomous frequency on cell position:

$$(4.1) \qquad \nu_n = \nu_0 - n\Delta\nu,$$

where $\nu_0$ is the pacemaker frequency, $\nu_n$ the frequency of cell $n$, and $\Delta\nu$ the frequency difference between neighbors, assumed constant for simplicity. The sequence of events occurring in cell $n$ is indicated in Figure 3. The cell signals at time $t = 0$ because it was signalled at time $\Delta t_s$ previously by cell $n - 1$. Cell $n$ remains refractory for a period $rT_n$ after it signals. It receives its next signal from cell $n - 1$ at $T_0 - \Delta t_s$ and then signals cell $n + 1$ at $T_0$, completing a cycle and restoring itself to the same state it was in at $t = 0$.

In the single-event model, I suppose that the only effect being signalled has on a cell is to shift the phase of its autonomous oscillation. After it has been signalled during its sensitive period, it signals $\Delta t_s$ later and enters its refractory period which is $rT_n$ and not $rT_0$. Thus the internal clock of the cell and its metabolism continue to run at the local rate characterized by the frequency $\nu_n$ after it has been signalled. The state of the cell clearly varies with time with the frequency $\nu_n$. Thus, when the cell is forced to signal again at time $T_0$ instead of $T_n$ it signals at a time when its cell state is different from what it would have been had it been signalling autonomously. Suppose I defined the phase of the cell's cycle at which signalling occurs in terms of the time interval between the actual signalling and the superceded autonomous signal:

$$(4.2) \quad \phi = (2\pi/T_n)(T_n - T_0) = 2(\pi\Delta\nu/\nu_0)n = n\Delta\phi.$$

Then this phase, which is a direct measure of cell state, increases linearly with position along the line of cells.

We have thus added a map to the clock. Time is measured in units of $T_0$, the period of the pacemaker and of the entire tissue, and position is measured in terms of the phase $\phi_n$, which is arrived at by comparing the local cell state at signalling with what it would have been had the signalling been autonomous. Of course, the frequency gradient by itself constitutes a map,

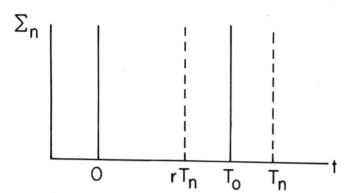

FIGURE 3. Time course of the concentration of the signalling agent in the $n$th cell for the single event model. Each pulse is idealized as a $\delta$-function. The period is that of the pacemaker cell, $n = 0$, $T_0$ by which the $n$th cell is entrained. $rT_n$ is the refractory period of the $n$th cell, and $T_n$ its autonomous period.

but would require frequency sensitive processes for its interpretation. Phase, on the other hand, is easy to interpret. The coincidence in time of two evanescent molecular species, one set by phase and one not, will do.

An elementary example will make the model clearer and more concrete. Suppose that the autonomous oscillator in each cell is in fact a relaxation oscillator. Suppose that a morphogen is manufactured in a cell at a constant rate proportional to the frequency of that cell,

$$(4.3) \qquad \dot{c}_n = c_M \nu_n,$$

where $c_M$ is a constant, the same for all cells. Suppose that signalling abruptly reduces the morphogen concentration to zero. Then, after signalling, the time course of $c_n$ is

$$(4.4) \qquad c_n = c_M \nu_n t.$$

Suppose that the cell is refractory until the concentration reaches the value $c_r$, which gives

(4.5)                    $r = c_r/c_M.$

If the cell is running autonomously, it will signal again when $t = T_n = 1/\nu_n$. The relaxation oscillator "fires" or "discharges" when the concentration $c_M$ is reached; $c_M$ is the maximum concentration in the cycle. This is summarized in Figure 4.

In fact cell $n$ does not run autonomously. It signals at time $T_0$, when the concentration is

(4.6)                    $c_n^* = c_M \nu_n/\nu_0.$

I have supposed in the single-event model that the measure of cell state which carries the position information is $\phi_n$ as given by equation (4.2). That definition is equivalent to

(4.7)            $\phi_n = 2\pi(c_M - c_n^*)/c_M = n\Delta\phi,$

from (4.6), which means that it is the difference between the maximum concentration of morphogen and the actual concentration reached which controls development.

This explicit and very simple model also makes clear the difference between the clock and map which constitute the control system for development and the developmental processes themselves. In each cell the concentration of morphogen varies during a period $T_0$ from zero to a value $c_n^*$ which decreases linearly with $n$. The difference $(c_M - c_n^*)$ constitutes the positional information which the cell then interprets by differentiating or moving according to its value of $(c_M - c_n^*)$. The time scale for setting up the positional information need have nothing to do with the time scale of its interpretation, and it is essential to recognize this when confronting experimental information.

Let us return now to discussion of the abstract version of the single-event model. Clearly, $T_0$ must exceed the refractory period of every cell in the tissue if the

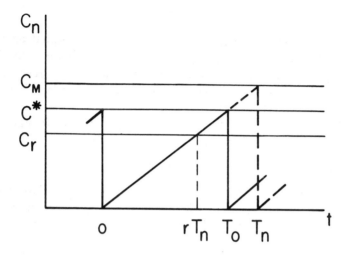

FIGURE 4. Time course of the morphogen concentration in the relaxation-oscillator illustration of the single-event model $c_M$ is the maximum concentration reached in autonomous oscillation. $c^*$ is the concentration reached when the $n$th cell is triggered by the $(n-1)$st. $c_r$ is the concentration below which the cell is refractory to signalling.

pacemaker is to entrain the entire tissue, or

(4.8)                    $$T_0 > rT.$$

This condition can be rewritten with the help of our earlier results in the form

(4.9)                    $$(\phi_N/2\pi) < 1 - r.$$

Now for maximum information carrying capacity, $\phi_N/2$ should be as close to unity as possible, certainly of order $\frac{1}{2}$. In the only case where there is any experimental evidence relating to the refractory period, that of the cellular slime molds D. discoideum and P. violaceum, $r$ does indeed appear to be about 1/3 to 1/2. With a refractory period of 1/2, $\phi_N$ would be at most about $\pi$. For typical fields of order 50–100 cells in linear extent,

$\Delta\nu/\nu_0$ would correspondingly be of order 0.5 to 1%, which is not a very large frequency gradient. In the case of the cellular slime mold slug and fruiting body, differentiation occurs into only 4 cell types, base plate, stalk, spore, and tip. This would require only a considerably smaller frequency gradient for adequate positional discrimination. On the other hand, for very fine detail, when the position of almost each cell must be specified, a less than 1% variation in phase from cell to cell may not be adequate and systems of greater informational capacity such as those discussed by Goodwin and Cohen may be necessary.

Finally, there is the question of regulation. We obviously have regulation in time, as the course of development is controlled by a phase $\phi_n$ which is proportional to time measured relative to a period. If, because of environmental perturbations, the $T_n$ change with time, development need not be perturbed because only the interpreting of phase and counting of periods need be involved. However, regulation in space would require that the phase shift $\phi_N$ be independent of $N$. From (4.2) $\phi_N$ depends only on $\nu_N$ and $\nu_0$.

$$(4.10) \qquad \phi_N = 2\pi(\nu_0 - \nu_N/\nu_0).$$

We require therefore that the frequency pattern regulate, that $\nu_0$ and $\nu_N$ be $N$-independent.

As has been emphasized to me by Goodwin [15], the active transport model of §2 would serve admirably for frequency regulation. It is only necessary that there be a linear or quasilinear relation between concentration and frequency, $\nu = \nu(c)$. The pacemaker frequency would always be $\nu(c_0)$ and $\nu_N$ would always be $\nu(c_1)$ or vice versa, independent of $N$. Goodwin's suggestion has the attractive feature that complicated developmental processes can be controlled through the phase of a periodic event which can have as much internal complexity as is required whereas concentration is used only for the control of frequency, a much simpler matter. There is in fact some experimental evidence that in the cellular slime molds, the single-event model with active transport regulation, or something much like it, does occur.

## 5. The phase-shift model

Only a very brief account of the phase-shift model is appropriate here as it is fully discussed in [2], in contrast to the single-event and active-transport models, which have not been described previously. The basic method followed by GC in building a model of a map based on propagating periodic events is to establish a local time or phase difference within each cell which is a function of the cell's position. This method was taken over in the previous section in the construction of the single-event model, where the time difference is the difference between time as kept by the pacemaker and the local time as kept by each individual cell after triggering by the $S'$-wave. The time difference is position dependent because of a gradient of autonomous (or local) $S$-event frequencies. Regulation is achieved by having the frequency gradient controlled by a concentration-gradient which in turn is controlled by the regulating active transport mechanism of §2, following a suggestion of Goodwin [15].

GC have a more complex realization of their basic idea of time difference as a function of position which has certain advantages over the single-event model. In addition to the $S$-event they introduce a second event, the $P$-event. In a free-running cell, the $P$-event occurs at a well-defined phase $\phi_0$ after the $S'$-event. They suppose that a triggered $S'$-event differs from an auto-nomous $S$-event in that the $P$-event does not occur automatically after it; it is in fact an $S'$-event. They suppose the existence of a signalling aspect of the $P$-event, as well as sensitive and refractory periods. However, they assume that the time delay between signalling and being signalled is greater for the $P$-event ($\Delta t_p$) than for the $S'$-event ($\Delta t_s$) so that the ensuing $P$-wave propagates more slowly than the $S'$-wave. The phase difference $\phi_{ps}$ between the $P$- and $S'$-events in a single cell then becomes a function of the position $r$ of that cell in the field, $\phi_{ps} = \phi_{ps}(r)$. This position dependence is determined from the wave equation

$$(5.1) \qquad\qquad (\nabla \phi_{ps})^2 = (\Delta \phi_{ps}^2/\xi d)^2,$$

$$(5.2) \qquad\qquad \Delta \phi_{ps} = \Delta \phi_p - \Delta \phi_s,$$

where $\Delta \phi_p$ and $\Delta \phi_s$ are the phase delay for signalling for the $P$- and $S$-events, respectively, subject to the same boundary conditions as for single organizing waves.

Thus in the GC model, the $S$-event provides the clock, and the position dependence of $\phi_{ps}$ provides the map. The positional information is present in the form of a 1-dimensional sequence of stacked surfaces of constant phase difference. The developmental axis is that tra-jectory orthogonal to the surfaces of constant phase difference which is of maximum length. Polarity is given by the sense of propagation of the organizing waves away from the pacemaker along the developmental axis. The 1-dimensional coordinate $x$ of each cell provided by this system is the distance from the pace-maker along the developmental axis to the intersection of the surface of constant $\phi_{ps}$ containing the cell with the axis.

The linear size of the field is the number of cells

along the developmental axis, $N$. If $N\Delta\phi_{ps}$ is $2\pi$, $\Delta\phi_{ps}$ returns to $\phi_0$, the value it started with at the pacemaker. As $N$ increases further, the map and therefore the pattern develop periodicity. The other models described here cannot give rise to periodic patterns. However, it is not difficult to modify the diffusion model to give periodic patterns via instabilities of the sort discussed by Turing [16] simply by introducing an appropriate dependence of the rate of production or destruction of the morphogen by the cell on its concentration. Nonpolar active transport models contain periodic solutions, as I shall discuss in a separate paper. In this way, one begins to approach in more biologically meaningful terms the notion of dissipative structures discussed extensively by Prigogine and co-workers [17] as well as similar results of Edelstein [18].

Regulation is even more important for the GC model because of the inevitability of periodicity when $N\Delta\phi_{ps} > 2\pi$. In aperiodic fields, $\Delta\phi_{ps}$ must therefore be less than $2\pi/N$ or $(\Delta\phi_{ps}/2\pi) < 1\%$ for a field of 100 cells. However, such a restriction on the magnitude of $\Delta\phi_{ps}$ is insufficient in itself for regulation, which requires that $\phi_{ps} = \phi_{ps}(x/L)$ where $L$ is the length of the developmental axis. GC introduce regulation through the action of a third event, the $R$- or regulating event. By means of the $R$-event, $\Delta\phi_{ps}$ is reduced with increasing $N$ so that the maximum phase difference $N\Delta\phi_{ps}$ cannot exceed some predetermined value $\phi_M$.

It is supposed by GC that subsequent developmental events depend on the particular value of $\phi_{ps}$ in a cell. To obtain finer detail in a pattern than is possible with the model as developed thus far and with an upper limit on $\Delta\phi_{ps}$ of $1\%$ of $2\pi$, GC have supposed that developmental events can be sensitive to pacemaker frequency as well. If the frequency gradient is sufficiently steep that the pacemaker period becomes shorter than the refractory period away from the pacemaker, the field breaks up into a set of subfields each with its own pacemaker frequency. Within each frequency step in this pattern, there can be a phase gradient as previously described. Thus the frequency steps provide a coarse coordinate system and the phase gradients a Vernier upon them. If the frequency gradient is maintained under the control of the regulating active transport mechanism of §2, the overall frequency step pattern regulates. This regulation of the frequency step pattern was not included in the original GC version.

A two-dimensional coordinate system requires two independent $P$-waves, one propagating from the pacemaker and the other from a second organizing center. According to GC, this latter differentiates after the original $S$- and $P$-wave propagation is established on the basis of the one-dimensional coordinate system thereby set up, plus some other gradient or asymmetry in the field, in accordance with the experimental observations. In the single-event model, a two-dimensional coordinate system requires two independent $S$-waves. In the diffusion or active transport models, a two-dimensional coordinate system requires two morphogens and two independent active transport systems operating roughly orthogonally. At this point, one begins to see further limitations in these models. The diffusion model requires further differentiation of a second set of sources and sinks and regulation becomes doubly difficult. To establish a concentration pattern with a geometry related to that of the embryo in a unique way requires pumping in a predetermined direction via the active transport system. This implies that the cells have a definite axial symmetry and polarity. For two dimensions one requires two orthogonal polarities, one for the transport of each morphogen. This implies a considerable internal structural complexity and specialization.

Transplant experiments in which an organizing center from one embryo is grafted onto a second embryo can be understood simply within the framework provided by the GC model. The two organizing centers are pacemakers. Organizing waves propagate outward from each until a boundary between the subfields controlled by each is established by refractoriness. A wide variety of illustrative applications of the GC model is provided in [2]. These should be read with the realization that in a number of cases the other models discussed here can also be applied with similar results, whereas in others only the GC model may do.

### 6. The phase diffusion model

Thus far we have discussed two classes of models: (1) transport models in which a morphogen or morphogen complex is transported by diffusion or actively, and the morphogen concentrations are quasistatic, and (2) organizing-wave models in which the morphogen or morphogen complex is periodic in concentration, and the phase of the oscillation is controlled by a wavelike propagation mechanism. In the active transport model, class (1), the morphogen concentration is given by

$$(6.1) \qquad \partial c/\partial t = - (\partial j(\nabla c)/\partial(\nabla c)): \quad \nabla^2 c + \dot{c},$$

for sufficiently low $|\nabla c|$, where $\dot{c}$ is rate of generation of morphogen, positive for $c < c_0$, negligible for $c_0 < c < c_1$, and negative for $c > c_1$ as discussed in §2. In the organizing-wave models, either the single-event or the Goodwin-Cohen case, the phase difference $\phi$ is governed by

(6.2)                    $\partial\phi/\partial t = v(\partial\phi/\partial n)$ ,

where $n$ is the coordinate normal to the surface of constant phase and $v$ is the propagation velocity $\xi d/\Delta t$, or by

(6.3)                    $(\nabla\phi)^2 = (\Delta\phi/\xi d)^2$ .

The boundary conditions are quite different in the two classes. The existence of tight junctions within a field but not between separate fields or tissues allows us to ignore transport of the morphogen out of the tissue so that $\nabla c = 0$ at the boundaries for class (1). The boundary conditions for class (2) follow from the refractory period and the Huyghens construction. There is no question but that the two classes of models lead to different coordinate surfaces within a field of given geometry. Nevertheless, it would be risky to try to infer which class of models was in fact applicable to a given embryo or developing organism from the purely spatial character of the emerging pattern. The predictions of (6.1) and (6.3), each with the appropriate set of boundary conditions, are in fact not so different in major features. The details in which they might differ could well be obscured by many effects present in the real systems and omitted for simplicity from the models.

To underscore this difficulty of distinguishing between control mechanisms with and without periodicity solely on the basis of emerging pattern alone, I develop in the present section a model in which the spatial dependence of the phase of a periodic event is controlled by diffusion. The model emerges from consideration of mitosis in Physarum polycephalum. In sufficiently small plasmodia of P. polycephalum mitosis is remarkably synchronous (Guttes, Guttes and Rusch [19]). Two separate pieces of plasmodium merge on contact.

Rusch et al. [20] have shown that if two equal sized pieces of plasmodium, one due for mitosis at, say, 1 p.m., and the other at 3 p.m., are merged, the nuclei of the resulting piece will undergo mitosis at 2 p.m. This plus additional experiments [20] provide strong presumptive evidence for the existence of a cytoplasmic agent controlling mitosis, a mitogen.

The simplest model one could construct would be the following. Mitosis is a periodic event. One can imagine a complex sequence of linked biochemical and mechano-chemical reactions which together constitute a mitotic oscillator. Part of the oscillatory cycle surely must take place in the cytoplasm in the vicinity of each nucleus, considering the complex of structural and mechanical events involved in mitosis. It may be at that point that the mitogen acts, its action may take place across the nuclear membrane, or it may be trans-ported into the nucleus. In any event, the mitogen controls the phase of the mitotic cycle.

To obtain the observed phase averaging upon fusion of two pieces of plasmodium, the phase $\phi$ of the mitotic cycle must be shifted by the mitogen to be linearly proportional to mitogen concentration $c$,

(6.4) $$\phi \propto c.$$

This implies a linear increase of mitogen concentration with time during the mitotic cycle. Mitosis is pre-sumably triggered when $c$ reaches some critical value $c_M$ at time $t_M$. Shortly after the time $t_M$ is reached, $c$ is presumably reduced to zero. Manufacture of the mitogen presumably resumes after mitosis is complete. Setting the origin of time at that point, we have

(6.5)
$$c = c_M t/t_M, \qquad 0 < t < t_M,$$
$$c = 0, \qquad t_M < t < T.$$

Correspondingly, the relation between phase and mitogen is

(6.6)
$$\phi = \phi_M c/c_M, \qquad 0 < \phi < \phi_M,$$
$$\phi_M = 2\pi t_M/T.$$

In summary, after mitosis is complete, the nucleus starts up the production of the mitogen in the cytoplasm. The concentration of mitogen increases linearly with time until a critical concentration $c_M$ is reached at time $t_M$. Mitosis then starts and the mitogen concentration is reduced to zero. Production of the mitogen starts again once mitosis is complete. The mitogen cycle is thus that of a relaxation oscillator.

When the plasmodium is larger than a certain critical size, mitotic synchrony can break down. A mitosis front is then observed propagating through the plasmodium. What has happened is that concentration differences of mitogen can arise over distances too large for them to be smoothed out by diffusion, active transport, or protoplasmic streaming during times short compared with $T$ or even $T - t_M$. I suppose for simplicity and definiteness that the mitogen is transported by diffusion instead of by active transport or protoplasmic streaming. $c$ then obeys the equation

(6.7)
$$\partial c/\partial t = D\nabla^2 c + \dot{c},$$

where

(6.8)
$$\dot{c} = (c_M/T_M) - c_M \sum_{n=0}^{\infty} \delta(t - t_M - nT)$$

upon ignoring the duration of mitosis. When the diffusion term is also ignored, this equation has as a particular one-dimensional solution

(6.9)
$$c(x,t) = \frac{c_M}{T}\left(t - n(x,t)\,T - t_0\,\frac{x}{L}\right),$$

where $n(x,t)$ is an integer satisfying

$$(6.10) \qquad \left(\frac{t}{T} - \frac{t_0}{T}\frac{x}{L} - 1\right) < n(x,t) < \left(\frac{t}{T} - \frac{t_0}{T}\frac{x}{L}\right),$$

$$(6.11) \qquad t_0 < T,$$

and $L$ is the length of the plasmodium. Equation (6.9) describes a plasmodium containing a mitotic phase gradient with at most one mitosis front which propagates at the rate

$$(6.12) \qquad v = L/t_0.$$

The velocity of propagation $v$ is proportional to the inverse of the phase gradient across the plasmodium,

$$(6.13) \qquad d\phi/dx = (2\pi/L)\,(t_0/T).$$

If we relax the restriction (6.11), which we may do by rewriting (6.9) in the form

$$(6.14) \qquad c(x,t) = \frac{c_M}{T}\left[t - \left(n(x,t) + \frac{x}{l}\right)T\right], \qquad l \leqq L,$$

then we describe a plasmodium in which there are at most $\mu$ mitosis fronts at any given time, where

$$(6.15) \qquad L/l - 1 \leqq \mu \leqq L/l.$$

Reinserting the diffusion term into (6.7), we find that (6.9) and (6.14) satisfy (6.7) everywhere except at the discontinuities in $n(x,t)$, the mitosis fronts. Diffusion there has the effect of smoothing out the discontinuity in concentration $(-c_M)$ across the mitotic front. To decide whether diffusion is important quantitatively, the distance $\Delta x_p$ the mitotic front propagates in time $\Delta t$ in the above model,

$$(6.16) \qquad \Delta x_p = v\Delta t \cong (L/T)\,\Delta t,$$

can be compared with the distance $\Delta x_D$ over which

the discontinuity is smoothed by diffusion in the same interval,

(6.17)                    $\Delta x_D = (D\Delta t)^{-1/2}.$

For diffusion to be unimportant, $\Delta x_D \ll \Delta x_p$ or $D \ll (L/T)\Delta x_p$ must hold. The upper limit for $\Delta x_p$ is $L$, so that unless

(6.18)                    $D \ll L^2/T$

holds, diffusion is important. If the mitogen diffuses freely through the cytoplasm and has a molecular weight of order 300, $D$ will be of order $5\times10^{-6}$cm$^2$/sec. $L$, on the other hand, is of order 1 cm and $T$ of order 20 hours so that $L^2/T \cong 1.4\times10^5$. The estimate of $(DT/L^2)^{-1/2}$ yielded by the preceding is about 0.8 indicating that diffusion is of an importance comparable to propagation in a 1 cm plasmodium. Plasmodia that are appreciably smaller should have synchronous mitoses throughout, as in fact observed (Mohberg and Rusch [21]).

I have discussed this model of the control of mitosis in Physarum polycephalum in such detail in the present context because it can be interpreted as a model of development. As such it plays a role intermediate between the organizing-wave models and the transport models. A periodic phenomenon takes place which can be utilized as a local developmental clock. The phase of the periodic phenomenon is controlled by the concentration of a molecular species which we might term a chronogen and which itself undergoes a relaxation oscillation. This control of phase leads to a tissue-wide correlation of the local clocks thereby establishing a global time. As fields are normally 100 cells in linear dimension and the pacemaker period in the range of minutes, $(DT/L^2)^{-1/2}$ is now of order 0.4 for a cell dimension of $10\mu$ and a period of 5 min. Diffusion therefore plays a significant role in controlling the phase of the oscillation, but not so much so that organizing wave propagation is ruled out. We thus have a model which within a parameter range appropriate to real cells shows a transition from phase diffusion to organizing wave propagation with no essential change in the spatial characteristics of the pattern. If active transport occurs instead of diffusion, a similar conclusion can be drawn. This indeed underscores the difficulty of distinguishing between quasistatic and periodic mechanisms for the control of development solely on the basis of emerging pattern.

I am grateful to Anthony Robertson for repeated encouragement and assistance during the course of this work, which was supported in part by the Office of Naval Research and the Alfred P. Sloan Foundation.

REFERENCES

1. L. Wolpert, J. Theoret. Biol. **25** (1969), 1.
2. B. C. Goodwin and M. H. Cohen, J. Theoret. Biol. **25** (1969), 49.
3. M. H. Cohen and A. Roberston, J. Theoret. Biol. **31**, (1971), 101.
4. _____. J. Theoret. Biol. **31**, (1971), 119.
5. J. T. Bonner, *The cellular slime molds,* 2nd ed., Princeton Univ. Press, Princeton, N. J., 1967.
6. T. Gustafson and L. Wolpert, Int. Rev. Cytology **15** (1963), 139; Biol. Rev. **42** (1967), 442.
7. See e.g. R. M. Gaze, M. J. Keating, G. Szekely and L. Beazley, Proc. Roy. Soc. B **175** (1970), 107.
8. B. I. Balinsky, *An introduction to embryology,* Saunders, Philadelphia, Pa., 1965.
9. J. S. Huxley and G. R. de Beer, *The elements of experimental embryology,* Cambridge Univ. Press, Cambridge, 1934.
10. C. M. Child, *Patterns and problems of development,* Univ. of Chicago Press, Chicago, Ill., 1941.
11. E. J. Furshpan and D. D. Potter, Current Topics in Dev. Biol. **3** (1968), 95.
12. H. Spemann, *Embryonic development and induction,* Yale Univ. Press, New Haven, Conn., 1938.
13. F. Crick, Nature **225** (1970), 420.
14. P. A. Lawrence, J. Exp. Biol. **44** (1966), 607.

**15.** B. C. Goodwin (private communication).

**16.** A. M. Turing, Philos. Trans. Roy. Soc. B **237** (1957), 37.

**17.** See e.g., I. Prigogine, in *Theoretical physics and biology,* M. Marois (editor), North-Holland, Amsterdam, 1969; I. Prigogine, R. Lefever, A. Goldbeter and M. Herschkowitz-Kaufman, Nature 223 (1969), 913.

**18.** B. Edelstein, J. Theoret. Biol. **26** (1970), 227.

**19.** E. Guttes, S. Guttes and H. P. Rusch, Dev. Biol. **3** (1961), 588.

**20.** H. P. Rusch, W. Sachsemeier, K. Behrens and V. Gruter, J. Cell. Biol. **31** (1966), 204.

**21.** J. Mohberg and H. P. Rusch, J. Bacteriol. **97** (1969), 144, found that a 14 cm plasmodium was nearly synchronous. Enhancement of the diffusion process by a factor of 4 through mixing by protoplasmic streaming could account for this discrepancy. An upper limit to the streaming contribution to an effective diffusion constant $D_{\text{eff}}$ is obtained by supposing that the streaming accomplishes complete mixing. The corresponding contribution to $D_{\text{eff}}$ is $\xi v^2 \nu$, where $\xi$ is between $1/4$ and $1/2$, $v$ is the streaming velocity, and $\nu$ the streaming period. The streaming velocity is of order $mm/\min$ and the period of order minutes, giving a value of $\xi v^2/\nu$ of order $10^{-5}$, which is large enough to account for the discrepancy.

# PERIODIC WAVE PROPAGATION AND PATTERN FORMATION: APPLICATION TO PROBLEMS IN DEVELOPMENT

By

## J. COOKE AND B. C. GOODWIN

*University of Sussex, England*

# 1. Introduction

The model presented by M. H. Cohen in the previous paper, describing how the propagation of periodic activity waves from cell to cell in a tissue can give rise to an information field which could direct the spatially and temporally organized course of early development, has features which make it particularly amenable to experimental test. The most obvious of these is the postulated occurrence of spatially localized pacemaker centres in embryos, resulting in the prediction that if such a centre can be simulated experimentally then it should be possible to reorganize the field or modify it in some way by altering the axes of positional information in the system. For each developmental system considered in this manner, it is necessary to decide on the organization of the system which is most likely in terms of the model; i.e., where the pacemaker is located, and where the surfaces of constant phase are expected to lie. In short, the application of the theory to any particular system requires the localization of the clocks and the construction of the postulated phase surfaces in a manner consistent with the known behaviour of the developmental system. We shall carry out this analysis very briefly, for illustrative purposes, for the case of the regeneration process in the fresh-water coelenterate, *Hydra littoralis*; and in more detail for the case of the much more complicated development of the amphibian gastrula.

## 2. Hydra: One-dimensional organization

The application of the phase-shift theory to the analysis of regeneration in hydra has already been presented in the paper by Goodwin and Cohen [4] which first described the theory. The present treatment of this system will be very brief, illustrating the principles of application and the experimental approach which arises from it. From studies by a number of different workers on the Hydrazoa (general review: Child [1]), it became evident that the region of highest organizational potential in the animal is the neighbourhood of the hypostome (Figure 1). For example, if a piece of tissue from the region just below the hypostome is grafted to the proximal end of a midgastric section (a section of the gastric region taken from just above the budding zone to a point about midway up the region), then the original axis of the gastric section will be reversed and the new hypostome will form from the subhypostomal tissue, peduncle and foot forming at the other, originally distal, end. If the midgastric section is allowed to regenerate on its own, however, the new hypostome invariably forms from the distal end, that end which was closest to the old hypostome, while the new peduncle forms from the proximal end. The gradient of autonomous S-event frequency postulated to be present in the animal will therefore have its high point at the distal extremity and decrease proximally. Thus under normal conditions distal tissue will always form the pacemaker region and consequently it will be the origin of the coordinate for axial positional information in this animal. The periodic S- and P-waves propagating proximally from the pacemaker define a polarity in the system, the direction in which the phase gradient increases. No periodicities of pattern occur along this axis of organization, so that the phase gradient has an extremum which is less than $2\pi$. The different regions shown in Figure 1 are then considered to arise as a result of the differentiation of cells in response to specific ranges of value of the phase gradient.

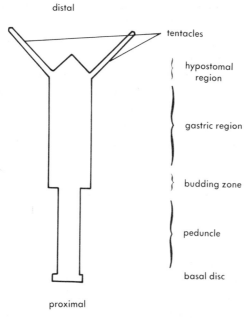

distal

tentacles

hypostomal region

gastric region

budding zone

peduncle

basal disc

proximal

FIGURE 1. Schematic diagram of *Hydra littoralis*

The obvious way to reorganize the regenerative axis in hydra is to produce a pacemaker by some experimental means at the "wrong" place in the regenerating tissue. According to the theory, the pacemaker could be simulated by some periodic stimulus which caused an activation of the $S$-event at the correct frequency. Since it is anticipated that the $S$-event is propagated from cell to cell ionically, a stimulus which caused a transient depolarization of cells in a localized region of the regenerating animal might be expected to act as an $S$-event activator. The stimulus which was tried in the case of hydra was short (150 msec) DC pulse of current delivered through a $40\mu$ platinum wire which passed through the tissue of the animal. If the voltage is high enough (3-4 volts), the tissue contracts. Pulses of lower voltage (1-2 volts) delivered at the right frequency (optimal, 1 per 2.5 mins) have been found to cause a defined perturbation of the regeneration process, amounting to a shift in the point of origin of the coordinate axis. These experiments will be in preparation reported elsewhere (Goodwin). The characteristics of the frequency response curve indicate that the periodic pulse is acting as a pacemaker by entraining the periodic $S$-event to its frequency. When the wire is placed proximally, the electrical signal should cause a reversal of the normal direction of wave propagation in the tissue, and so cause a reversal of normal polarity. Such a reversal is observed, but it is incomplete, showing that the signal used does not fully simulate the normal hypostomal organizing center. This can be understood in terms of the coupling between phase angle and changes in autonomous frequency in the tissue, a problem which was not considered in the original paper but which will receive detailed consideration in a forthcoming publication.

This investigation in hydra illustrates the basic principles which underlie the design of experiments which seek to test some of the basic assumptions of the theory. The regeneration field in hydra is particularly simple from the point of view of the phase-shift model, the surfaces of constant phase being sections of circles with center at the distal tip of the regenerating tissue and radii cutting the longitudinal axis of the cylindrical regenerate at right angles. A much more complicated developmental field is that which is involved in the fundamental spatial organization of the mesodermal tissues of the amphibian embryo. The surfaces of constant phase in this field must involve at least two axes and hence two wave propagation centers. We will now consider how the spatial pattern of cell differentiation which is observed in this embryo can be explained on the basis of the phase-shift theory. It is necessary first to give a description of the relevant embryological details.

*The spatial organization of the early amphibian embryo.*

The earliest stage of amphibian development consists of a rapid series of cell cleavages which proceeds until there are some $10^4$ cells organized in the shape of a hollow sphere known as a blastula, with walls 3-4 cells thick surrounding an eccentrically placed cavity. The eccentric position of this cavity, the blastocoel, which is displaced towards the upper side of the blastula, is due to differences in the size of the cells, the largest cells being at the lower (vegetal) pole while the smallest are at the upper (animal) pole. This ordered distribution of cell size arises from a gradient of cell division rate, maximal at the animal pole and minimal at the vegetal pole, this in turn being due to a graded distribution of yolk content in the egg cytoplasm, maximal at the vegetal and minimal at the animal pole, the yolk interfering physically with the division process. Thus cleavages in the early embryo are not synchronous after the first two or three.

A second axis in the early embryo arises from the existence of a localized area of surface cytoplasm in the fertilized egg known as the grey crescent, located somewhat below the equator and thought to be determined in relation to the point of sperm entry. Physico-chemical properties are almost certainly imparted to cells receiving part of this piece of egg surface, such that at a certain point on the surface of the mature blastula, known as the dorsal lip, in a latitude nearer the vegetal pole, the cell movements of gastrulation commence (see next section). The great circle passing through the middle of the grey crescent and the animal pole defines a plane of bilateral symmetry in the blastula.

By this time, the area of the presumptive dorsal lip is a regulative field, in that if the cells including it are removed the organization of the blastula will be reconstituted, so that other cells alter their normal fate in development to become an active dorsal lip (Curtis [2]). Visible evidence of a bilateral organization, with an altered gradient of cell size and cell properties along meridians passing close to the dorsal lip, as compared with those passing ventrally, varies in intensity between different species at this stage.

The onset of the local cell movements with which gastrulation commences may be caused either by the lapse of a certain absolute amount of time since initiation of cleavage (i.e. by programming at the cell level) or by the achievement of a certain cell number in the blastula. Experiments to distinguish between these two alternatives have not yet been performed.

By the method of dye-marking small groups of cells on the late blastula, and following their subsequent fate, the type of map shown in Figure 2a has been constructed for many species. A map, delimiting various regions on the blastula on the basis of their developmental capabilities when removed *at this point in time* from their normal interactions with other areas (i.e. cultured as explants under various conditions), is much simpler than such a fate map, however (Figure 2b). Holtfreter has been largely responsible for such maps in newt species (Holtfreter [5]). The large area surrounding the animal pole, labelled atypical epidermis, has the capacity to self-differentiate only into an atypical version of the double-layered epithelium of cells (the epidermis) which normally comes to surround the later embryo. The sheets of cells formed by cultures from this region also show a slight spontaneous tendency to increase their area.

The band of cells at the vegetal edge of the last area,

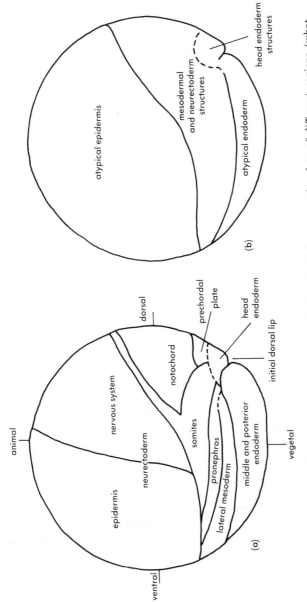

FIGURE 2. The urodele gastrula seen from the side showing (a) presumptive fate of different regions (what they will normally develop into) and (b) what the regions will self-differentiate into when parts are isolated in saline.

which is broadest in the meridian of the dorsal lip which lies at its ventral margin, is more heterogeneous in properties. It corresponds to the presumptive mesoderm layer and (in the immediate vicinity of the dorsal lip) to the head endoderm. Cultured explants develop to form histologically recognizable structures of the mesoderm, and also (especially in large groups of cells) of ectoderm and nervous system. The head endoderm, lying also above the dorsal lip, may produce in isolation structures recognizably belonging to its normal fate (pharynx with gill slits).

Comparison of Figure 2a with 2b shows that the determination of cells of the presumptive mesoderm at this stage is very labile and generalized. They constitute a field, such that, if some of the presumptive areas defined on 2a are extirpated, other cells will finally alter their own fate to restore the total organ-forming capacity of the cell mass. Slight evidence of polarity is noted by most workers on the late blastula and very early gastrula, however, in that cell groups from nearer the dorsal meridian, cultured in isolation, tend to produce structures corresponding both to their own presumptive fate *and* to that of cell groups more ventral, whereas the latter tend to differentiate only according to their own fate. This tendency is easily reversed, however, by transplanting cells within the field. For a discussion of the concepts embraced by the use of the term "field" in theories and descriptions of development, see Waddington's "Organizers and Genes" (Cambridge University Press, 1940) [12, Chapter 12].

Explants of presumptive mesoderm tend to undergo marked cellular movements and shape changes, which bear some relationship to those that are their fate in the whole blastula during gastrulation. Some cells go through a cycle of adhesiveness and motility such that they get into the interior of the cell masses and these usually develop the mesodermal structures, whereas those remaining outside, in large explants, become neurecto-dermal in character. Thus, it should be noted that the presumptive neurectoderm is delimited by the fact that, at this stage, it possesses the capacity to develop in iso-lation into *no* typical structure, whereas parts of the mesodermal field, and even of the presumptive head endoderm, are capable of giving rise to structures corresponding to *its* presumptive fate. The whole early gastrula is labile in organization in the sense that groups of cells from anywhere, transplanted within it, will assume successfully the normal fate of their new sur-roundings.

There is controversy in the literature (Holtfreter and Hamburger [7]; Waddington, [11]) with respect to the spontaneous differentiative tendency of cells from the remaining, circular region of the mature blastula, vegetal to the latitude of the dorsal lip. Holtfreter maintained that such cells already developed rather strictly according to fate (the various regions of middle and posterior endodermal gut lining), and were no longer even able to assume the fate of artificially introduced new sur-roundings, whilst other workers have suggested that their subsequent development is largely dependent upon the pattern existing within the mesoderm, against which they come to lie during gastrulation.

Figure 3a shows the movements of gastrulation which, commencing at the dorsal lip, convert the embryo into a structure having three discrete layers of cells. The mechanics of gastrulation are still not fully elucidated experimentally, but the whole process can be accounted for by a sequence of cell behaviour changes whereby the presumptive axial, then finally lateral and ventral meso-derm cells become, in turn, unadhesive for the "coat" which lies at the surface of the embryo, then very ad-hesive for themselves and locomotory. Meanwhile, the neurectoderm stretches in an animal-vegetal direction on the dorsal part of the sphere, and then laterally during the later part of the process as the mass of endoderm plus mesoderm becomes progressively enclosed within it. The yolky endodermal mass remains cohesive, whilst the mesodermal mantle migrates, as a sheet, in around the edges of the dorsal lip (which finally becomes the circular blastopore) and then between the ectoderm and the endoderm (from which latter it splits ventrally in order completely to envelop it).

At the end of this process, the embryo as a whole rotates under influence of gravity through somewhat more than 90°, due to the yolky endoderm. The original animal-vegetal axis, within the neurectoderm area, is transformed to an antero-posterior one between the region of the presumptive head (first intucked cells) and that of the final blastopore (Figure 3b). The significance of the term dorso-ventral for the other axis, within the crescentic area of the presumptive mesodermal mantle on the blastula surface, is revealed by its final orientation in the gastrula. Since this area is transformed into a nearly cylindrical sheath of cells, the term mediolateral may now be applied when referring to positions near to, or away from, the dorsal axis of the embryo when viewed from the dorsal aspect.

During intucking the bilateral symmetry of the embryo must be preserved by the mesodermal and head endodermal cells migrating straight towards the animal pole (future head end). Evidence suggests that the intrinsic antero-posterior (animal-vegetal) stretching seen in the neurectoderm is also expressed within the organization of the dorsal lip at this stage, since transplanted dorsal lips have a strong tendency to maintain their own direction of intucking and migration of cells (Holtfreter and Hamburger [7]) despite movements of host cells.

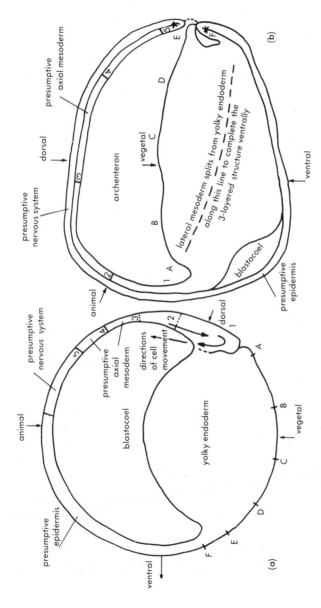

FIGURE 3. The urodele gastrula in section, showing (a) gastrulation movements which result in the reloca-
tion of the numbered and lettered regions in the late gastrula as shown in (b).

Groups of cells of the mesodermal mantle, isolated before intucking from the surface of the gastrula, show a spontaneous tendency to perform the movements in which they would normally have participated. The presumptive mesodermal mantle is a labile field in the same sense that a nonaxial piece of dorsal lip, used as a transplant, will regulate if large enough to produce a bilaterally symmetrical mass of intucked cells (as shown by subsequent histological differentiation).

In view of the theory to be presented, it should be held in mind that the lip around which cells are rolling as they invaginate during gastrulation (known as the *blastopore*), is *not* a cellular entity but a dynamic position. Topologically, cells within the interior of a midperiod gastrula form a continuous adherent sheet with those on the surface.

Starting towards the end of gastrulation, which itself lasts several hours in most species, the rudiment of the nervous system is laid down by the delimitation of an approximately pear-shaped area on what is now the dorsal side of the gastrula, its narrow end at the closing blastopore and its broad anterior end at the presumptive head region. Neurectoderm within this area changes its epithelial structure to one of tall columnar cells, then slowly sinks between raised ridges that form at its periphery. The latter finally fuse to leave a long, narrow tube of epithelium, having a small lumen, and underlying the ectoderm on the dorsal side of the embryo. The ectoderm now becomes the epidermis of the animal, and the tube, the brain and spinal cord. The various regions of the nervous system differentiate according to their position on an axis running through the material in an anterior-posterior direction. After its first formation, the various regions of the *neural plate*, then *neural tube*, are labile in their differentiation capacities, i.e. they may be transplanted between different levels of the whole rudiment without affecting the final pattern produced. Soon, however, the anterior-posterior structure becomes determined.

Extensive experimentation since the work of Spemann and Mangold [10] has confirmed that both the initial stimulus, causing development of the dorsal area of neurectoderm into nervous tissue rather than epidermis, and then the positional information whereby the neural plate subsequently develops its normal pattern, are provided by the axial part of the mesodermal mantle that comes to underlie the prospective nervous system during gastrulation. The process, known as primary *embryonic induction*, has the following salient features:

(1) By far the greater weight of evidence indicates that the field of positional information, whereby the pattern of the neural plate is specified, exists as a feature of the inductive activity of the underlying axial mesoderm, rather than being latent within the ectoderm itself. It also appears, at least for the initial, broad level of specification of parts of the nervous system rudiment (*regionalisation*), that the induced neurectoderm does not erect within itself a completely regulatory field of positional information, but rather responds to such information as is locally present in the underlying mesoderm. The latter appears to be a regulatory field at its first formation (in the late blastula, before its intucking and, in some species, during the middle part of gastrulation), but becomes partially *mosaic* or locally determined, when it has reached its final position in the normal course of development. The evidence for these statements is as follows:

Early dorsal lips, implanted into the ventral regions of a host gastrula, themselves invaginate and at the same time organize the surrounding mesodermal cell sheet of the host to produce a secondary mesodermal field. A secondary neural plate, often complete and normal in proportions (although it may be smaller over-all then normal), is then induced. This may occur in any part of the ectoderm of young gastrulae, and there exists only a moderate tendency for secondary axial structures to arise in close parallel with the host's axis.

Late dorsal lips, or parts of the final neurula mesoderm used as grafts, however, tend only to organize host tissue into part of the normal mesodermal axial field (as defined by subsequent tissue structure). In such cases, part only of the normal neural pattern appears in the overlying ectoderm.

(2) There is much evidence (Saxen and Toivonen [9], Niewkoop and van der Grinten [8]) that the initial inductive stimulus determining neural development is a diffusible substance passing between mesodermal and neurectodermal layers, and that the positional information for regionalisation consists of a gradient with respect to the relative amount(s) of at least one further substance, given out by the various parts of the mesodermal axis, and modifying the character of the neural development of the recipient cells. These substances are as yet poorly defined, but differ in their diffusion and thermostability characteristics. Correlations among the incomplete mesodermal and then neural structures produced after grafting of late, and therefore determined, parts of the inducing field (see above) suggest that the inducing action of particular parts of the axial mesodermal strip is correlated exactly with the final tissue type (e.g. notochord, head mesoderm, tail somites) into which they subsequently differentiate.

(3) The period during which explanted cells of the presumptive neurectoderm are competent to react to any inductive stimulus, by becoming determined to form nervous tissue, both begins *and ends* after certain elapsed

times since onset of development of the embryo from which they drive. Neural development at the visible level, even in induced cells, never sets in until near the end of this period of competence. In other words, it appears that cells are subject to a continuously unfolding programme of internal states in the absence of particular stimuli, their history in terms of position within the embryo, and/or inductive stimuli received, merely determining the choice of pathway at various critical points in the programme.

(4) Models have been proposed which explain the initial neural plate shape as a function of the time course of invagination of the axial mesoderm under the dorsal neurectoderm, together with the diffusion properties of the primary inducing substance and thresholds of reactivity in the target tissue. However, in experiments with the various known abnormal, nonliving, inducing substances, although structures typical of the normal nervous system at the cell level are often seen, large parts of the normal, organized pattern of the neural field seem not to be produced (Waddington [11]).

The structure of the embryo at the close of the period of regionalisation of the nervous system rudiment, i.e. of the early neurula, is shown in Figure 4.

The mesodermal mantle then, by the time it has finished its invagination, contains positional information, together with the capacity to express it, sufficient to specify the development of the main organ systems of the animal in their normal spatial relationships. As has been mentioned, the endoderm (apart from the head endoderm which is self-organizing and effectively part of the mesodermal mantle) is often thought to receive its positional information as inductive stimuli from the mesoderm which comes to lie adjacent to it. The field properties of the mesoderm are partially lost during the process of its invagination as a coherent sheet, so that in the early

neurula or late gastrula, although no visible differentiation has yet taken place, the developmental potencies of
explanted pieces of presumptive mesoderm are much more
definite and restricted than they were in the same field
when on the blastula. The properties of the mesodermal
mantle at the close of gastrulation, relative to those at its
beginning, are roughly as follows:

(1) There appear to be two axes along which positional
information exists, such that pieces removed and cultured separately do not regulate to produce structure
corresponding to the whole of these axes, although they
give rise to more than what was their presumptive fate
when *in situ*. The first of these is antero-posterior (i.e.
in a direction corresponding to the original animal-
vegetal gradient of the blastula). Thus antero-ventral
material when isolated has a strong tendency to form
recognizable heart structures, whilst more posterior cell
groups produce blood-forming tissue characteristic of
the mesodermal walls of the body cavity in later embryos.
Antero-dorsal material tends to form head mesoderm,
whilst progressively more postero-dorsal explants show an
increasing tendency to form notochord (precursor of the
axial skeleton), then somite (muscle forming) material,
which is normally most prominent at the tail end of
neurulae. Dorsally, the gradient also exists with respect
to the power, on the part of implanted parts of the mesodermal mantle, to organize more mesoderm into a secondary axial field, and thus induce secondary central
nervous structure in overlying ectoderm. Such secondarily
organized embryos, formed in early gastrula hosts by
implantation of parts of the axial mesoderm of late
gastrulae or neurulae, are incomplete along their antero-
posterior axes according to the position of origin of the
graft.

The regulative organization, whereby lateral parts

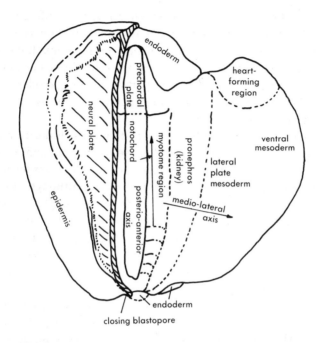

FIGURE 4. The urodele neurula, showing the spatial organization of regions in the mesodermal mantle and the two-dimensional axial system.

of the young mesodermal mantle, when grafted or explanted into culture, will assume an axial-symmetrical structure with respect both to their own differentiation and to their inductive power, is also lost at the neurula stage. Inductive power now falls off more steeply in a lateral direction. This is one expression of the loss of regulative capacity in the second, medio-lateral, axis.

Pieces explanted from various positions, medially or laterally, but from one antero-posterior level within the neurula, differentiate according to presumptive fate in a much more definite manner than was the case for the early gastrula mesoderm. There is, however, still a generally observed tendency for more medial pieces to regulate to form also more lateral parts of the field. Also, ventral explants may have their development altered from presumptive fate in a "dorsal" direction, if cultured next to a presumptively much more dorsal part of the same age (Yamada [12]).

Various groups of amphibian species differ with respect to the time at which the mesodermal mantle loses its completely regulative field properties. Thus in frog species, complete antero-posterior inductive capacity for the central nervous system can no longer be achieved by *pieces* taken from the region of the presumptive axial mesoderm, above the dorsal lip, at the beginning of gastrulation, whereas in some newt species, large sections of the intucked axis may be artifically reversed in polarity, and regulation still ensures to give normal development. Experimentation on the transition from field to mosaic determined properties of the embryo during this period is still very fragmentary.

Various areas of the neurectoderm outside the neural plate nevertheless differentiate into accessory structures which finally co-ordinate with localized parts of the central nervous system, e.g. placodes of the nose and ear rudiments and parts of the cranial nerve ganglia. (In at least one species, also, the presumptive eye lens epithelium is determined before contact with the eye rudiment from the brain.) There is again no evidence that positional information axes within the ectodermal sheet specify the positions of these areas, however. Rather, it appears that their position is inductively dependent upon patterns of interaction between head endoderm and mesoderm beneath the epidermis, before the specific inductive stimuli from outgrowing parts of the central nervous system come into operation, at stages beyond those covered in this paper.

### 3.  Axes and surfaces of constant positional information in the mesodermal mantle

The above description and analysis of amphibian development up to the early neurula leads, then, to the conclusion that the primary informational axes for the development of ectodermal and mesodermal tissues are to be found in the mesodermal mantle. We will now give an interpretation of the sequence of events which could explain the origin and location of these axes, and hence the shape of the surfaces which determine the spatial pattern of cell differentiation in the neurula.

In the original article on the phase-shift model, it was proposed that the observed distribution of differentiation potential in the early gastrula could be explained on the basis of a pacemaker and $P_1$-propagation centre at the animal pole of the embryo and a $P_2$-propagation centre in the neighbourhood of the dorsal lip, the grey crescent region. The exact size of these centres is not particularly significant for the location of surfaces of constant phase required to explain the observed boundaries between epidermis and chordamesoderm on the one hand, and chordamesoderm and endoderm on the other. So we may assume that they are fairly extensive, as shown in Figure 5. It was assumed that these propagation centres derive their properties from the biochemical composition of the cells in the regions shown as $C_1$ and $C_2$. As cells migrate during the process of invagination and the movements of gastrulation, it is to be expected that they will carry with them the substances conferring upon them their particular properties, so that the centres will change both their positions and their shapes, due to differential cell migration. In particular, the cells originally in the $C_2$ region will move in through the blastopore and travel anteriorly inside the gastrula. Since the most active migration and stretching of cells occurs in the midline, the $C_2$ region will become elongated during invagination. The whole of this region eventually disappears inside the blastopore and occupies an elongated elliptical region stretching from the animal pole to a point not far from the blastopore.

In the meantime, the cells of the $C_1$ region stream towards the blastopore, the most active migration and stretching occurring along the great circle joining the blastopore to the animal pole. Towards the end of gastrulation, cells which originally occupied the boundary of $C_1$ closest to the dorsal lip of the blastopore will in fact come to lie close to this opening. $S$-waves propagating from this region will pass in through the blastopore and travel on through the invaginated tissue. (There is good reason to believe that waves cannot travel directly from ectoderm to mesoderm in a radial direction, and this assumption is made throughout.) The blastopore thus becomes the origin of $S$- and $P_1$-waves for the invaginated tissue, the mesodermal mantle. The loss of the $P_2$-propagation centre from the surface of the late gastrula and the spreading of the pacemaker region means that the original two dimensions of positional information which were present in the early gastrula are virtually reduced to one. $P_2$-waves propagating out from the blastopore, arising from the now internalized region $C_2$, will spread out from the blastopore and intersect at very shallow angles with the surfaces of constant $\phi_{P_1 S}$, giving poor resolution of phase angle over the ectoderm. According to this interpretation, the reason why the ectoderm has such weak organizational potential is because of the absence of the $P_2$-propagation centre from the surface, so that the tissue is unable to organize itself in two dimensions.

Within the mesodermal mantle, however, the picture is quite different. When this tissue is spread out in a flat sheet, it has the shape shown in Figure 6. Here we show

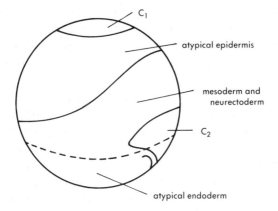

FIGURE 5. The early urodele gastrula showing the postulated locations of the pacemaker and $P_1$-propagation center, $C_1$, and the $P_2$-propagation center. $C_2$. The dotted line is a surface of constant phase, $\phi_{P_1 S}$, while the solid line is a surface of constant phase, $\phi_{P_2 S}$. These surfaces separate regions of different developmental potential as shown in Figure 2b.

the postulated position of the $C_2$ region after invagination and the effective pacemaker region which is the dorsal boundary of the blastopore. The locus of points 0 on the surface of constant phase difference $\phi_{P_2 S}$ are defined by the expression

$$n/v_1 + n_2/v_2 + t_0 - n_1/v_1 = \text{const.}$$

where

$n_1$ is the distance of 0 from the boundary of $C_1$,

$n_2$ is the distance of 0 from the boundary of $C_2$,

$n$ is the distance from the boundary of $C_2$ to the point $M$,

$v_1$ is the velocity of propagation of the $S$-event,

$v_2$ is the velocity of propagation of the $P_2$-event, and

$t_0$ is a constant, the time between the occurrence of $S$ and the initiation of $P_2$ in $C_2$.

If we make the assumption that the $S$-wave travels much more rapidly than the $P_2$-wave, i.e. $v_1 \gg v_2$, then we get the surfaces of constant phase $\phi_{P_2 S}$ like those shown by the solid lines. The surfaces of constant phase $\phi_{P_1 S}$ are shown as dotted lines. The axis of the $\phi_{P_1 S}$ surfaces is the line drawn from $C_1$ through the middle of $C_2$. This defines the posterio-anterior axis. From the midpoint of $C_2$, axes have been drawn cutting the surfaces $\phi_{P_2 S}$ at right angles. This shows the polarity of the medio-lateral axes. There is obviously bilateral symmetry about the posterio-anterior axis.

The two sets of surfaces of constant phase provide a two-dimensional grid of positional information over the mesodermal mantle. Referring to Figure 4 for the actual spatial arrangement of the regions of different developmental fate in the mesoderm, it is evident that there is a fairly good correspondence between the regions except for the boundary between the myotome region and the pronephros region in the neighbourhood of the blastopore. This boundary cannot be specified solely by a $\phi_{P_2 S}$ surface of the kind drawn. It is important to remember at this point, however, that the pattern of regional differentiation in embryos arises not only from the existence of global fields, but from local interactions between tissues as well. It is known that the notochord is an inducer of somite differentiation, so that the shape of the myotome region could be a result of both global and local effects, the extension of this region across the $\phi_{P_2 S}$ boundary as drawn between $C_1$ and $C_2$ being a local inductive effect. Regions such as that forming the heart correspond to a domain specified by a range of values of both $\phi_{P_1 S}$ and $\phi_{P_2 S}$.

The experimental investigation of the theory as applied to the spatial and temporal organization of the amphibian gastrula requires the introduction of a perturbation which will specifically reorganize the field of positional information in the mesodermal mantle. Since this tissue is inside

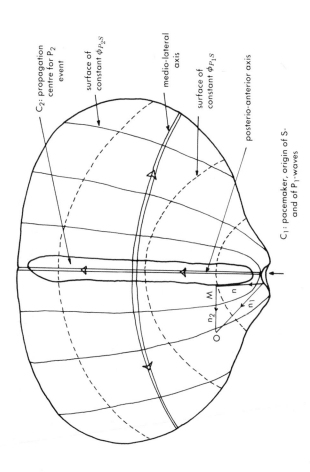

FIGURE 6. The postulated two-dimensional organization of the mesodermal mantle, resulting from wave propagation originating in the regions $C_1$ and $C_2$, with surfaces of constant phase as shown.

the gastrula, and since it is supposed that $S$- and $P$-waves do not propagate from ectoderm to mesoderm except via the blastopore, any pacemaker simulator must be introduced into the tissue of the mantle itself if it is to cause an alteration of the axes. An anteriorly located pacemaker would reverse the posterio-anterior axis, but have little effect on the medio-lateral axis. Such a perturbation would be difficult to achieve because the mesodermal field undergoes a continuous change of shape due to cell movement, and there is no topographically stationary point of the anterior mesoderm where a perturbation simulating pacemaker activity could be introduced. What would make the whole investigation greatly simplified would be some exteriorization of the mesoderm, making it accessible to direct perturbation.

Fortunately there is an alternation of normal gastrulation which results in precisely this phenomenon. It is known as exogastrulation, and it can be caused by a defined variation in the ionic strength of the medium in which the embryos develop. Instead of the presumptive mesodermal tissues tucking into the blastocoel, they carry out an abortive invagination, migrating to the blastoporal region and then moving outwards so that their direction of movement is nearly 180° away from the normal direction. This results in the mesodermal mantle forming outside, independently of the normal relation with the ectoderm, which collapses into a rather shapeless mass of tissue. Differentiation of various mesodermal regions then proceeds in a manner similar to the normal pattern; but most of the ectodermal structures, now deprived of their normal spatial relations with the mesoderm, fail to differentiate. This observation in itself constitutes strong evidence in favour of the view that it is in the mesoderm that the two-dimensional field of positional information develops, not in the ectoderm.

Exogastrulae, then, would be the obvious experimental material to work with in attempting to reorganize the axes of the mesodermal field. There are, however, other methods of approach which involve working with parts of the gastrula, known as explants. These have a degree of developmental autonomy also, which it should be possible to change by the appropriate localized perturbation. The stimulus being used in these studies, which are being carried out with embryos of *Xenopus laevis*, the South African toad, is an electric field applied to a small region of the embryonic tissue. The electrodes, which are made of $40\mu$ platinum wire, are not pushed into the tissue as they were in the work with hydra, but are placed in close proximity to the cells. A local electric field is then generated which, it is hoped, will result in a local depolarization of the cell membranes and initiate the $S$-process, which should then propagate from the stimulated region. The prediction is that when the stimulus is delivered at the correct frequency, then a pacemaker centre will be simulated and a new origin of the axis for phase information $\phi_{P_1 S}$, will have been established, resulting in a reorganized embryonic field.

There are other stimuli which could be used to simulate pacemaker activity, but the simplicity of generating an electric field and controlling its frequency, together with the success of this stimulus in causing a perturbation in hydra, recommend it as an experimental probe. Another approach to the theory is to look for periodicities in the developing tissue by the use of microelectrodes, for example. This is technically a good bit more difficult than the introduction of electrical or other stimuli, but it would provide very direct evidence for the existence of pacemaker activity of some kind. The existence of pacemakers in embryonic neural tissue has of course already been established by experiments such as those of Hamburger and Balaban [6] and Cunningham [3] in the chick. But the phase-shift theory predicts that periodic activity waves of a more general kind, not requiring specialized nerve cells for their generation and propagation, are a universal embryological phenomemon. The number and variety of experiments suggested by this prediction is large, and we have explored only a small corner of the field in this publication. However, we hope that the general principles involved in the application of the phase-shift theory to developmental systems, the type of geometrical and analytical problem which emerges, and some methods of experimental investigation, will have become evident from this exercise.

#### REFERENCES

1. C. M. Child, *Patterns and problems of development,* Univ. of Chicago Press, Chicago, Ill., 1941.
2. A. S. G. Curtis, Endeavour **22** (1963), 134.
3. A. W. B. Cunningham, J. Gen. Physiol. **45** (1962), 1065.
4. B. C. Goodwin and M. H. Cohen, J. Theoret. Biol. **25** (1969), 49.
5. J. Holtfreter, Roux' Archiv Entw. Mech. **133** (1936), 427.
6. V. Hamburger and M. Balaban, Devel. Biol. **7** (1963), 533.
7. J. Holtfreter and V. Hamburger, *Analysis of development,* Saunders, Philadelphia, Pa., 1955, p. 230.
8. P. D. Niewkoop and S. J. van der Grinten, Embryologia **6** (1961), 51.
9. L. Saxen and S. Toivonen, *Primary embryonic induction,* Logos Press, London, 1962.
10. H. Spemann and H. Mangold, Arch. Micr. Anat. a. Entw. Mech. **100** (1926), 599.
11. C. H. Waddington, *Organizers and genes,* Cambridge Univ. Press, New York, 1940.
12. T. Yamada, Zoological Magazine (Tokyo) **57** (1947), 124.

# THE ORGANIZATION OF
# CELLULAR GENETIC CONTROL SYSTEMS

By

## STUART   KAUFFMAN

*University of Chicago*

# Contents

# 1. Introduction

Several years ago the late mathematician John von Neumann remarked that the study of complex systems composed of many parts could profitably be decomposed into two complementary tasks: the elucidation of the mechanisms and laws of the individual parts; and the no less important and difficult task of analysis of the organization of the parts into a functioning whole. There can be no doubt that recent advances in molecular and cellular biology in understanding not only the chemical structure of DNA, RNA, and protein but also in elucidating some of the mechanisms controlling transcription, translation, and enzyme activity, must soon bring to the foreground questions of how these processes are integrated. Unfortunately, our theories here are less richly developed than those concerned with the chemical mechanisms of the parts.

The purpose of this article is to try to state explicitly at least some of the tasks the integrated gene control system seems to accomplish, to develop a theory which allows us to see some ways that control systems might work, to discuss implications of the theory for the kinds of control functions which molecular mechanisms that regulate transcription, translation and enzyme activation might follow, that would yield systems whose global behavior is as orderly as cells', to evaluate several predictions from the theory, and to attempt to find various empirical approaches to test them. The emphasis of the article is on the urgent need for theories about the ways in which integrated genetic control systems might function.

## 2. Global behaviors of gene control systems

It is now clear that both prokaryotes and eukaryotes are capable of controlling the onset and cessation of DNA synthesis, transcription, translation, and enzyme activity–in many cases of quite specific species of molecules, (Jacob and Monod [23], Shires, Kauffman and Pitot [35], Tomkins [36]). The molecular mechanisms accomplishing these tasks may not be identical in prokaryotes and eukaryotes; for example, no "classical" operon has been found in a eukaryote, whose transscription regulation may involve acetylation of chromosome bound histones (Allfrey [1]) or other mechanisms. We will refer to the system of controls concerning DNA replication, transcription of particular genes, translation of particular mRNA, and enzyme activity as the integrated gene control system. However these processes are controlled in metazoans, a central tenet of current biology is that cells in an organism differ predominately due to differential biosynthetic activity, not usually due to loss of genetic material. Attempts to frame theories about the integration of these still only partially known components might well begin with a clear statement of apparently global behaviors of cellular gene control systems which might be hoped to reflect something of the control system's organization.

Several characteristics of the behavior of metazoan gene control systems are so ubiquitous that they are rarely mentioned; nevertheless, precisely because of their ubiquity, they are likely to be of fundamental importance. Perhaps the most obvious of these is the apparently constrained dynamic behavior of metazoan gene control systems. Consider that a metazoan cell may have perhaps 100,000 or more different genes. Suppose each gene is only capable of being active or inactive, and ignore for the moment activities of mRNA and protein. Then a metazoan cell with only 100,000 genes has $2^{100,000} \cong 10^{30,000}$ conceivable different states of gene activity. At known rates of alteration of gene activity, a cell could not explore that dynamic space in billions of times the history of the universe. Just how minuscule a subset of patterns of gene activity a given cell type is restricted to is entirely unknown, but presumably it is very small, since we manage to recognize the same cell type over time and cell divisions.

Even if an organism has, say, 100 cell types, these jointly would seem to be restricted to a very small subset of the enormous potential variation in gene activity.

Whatever the criteria by which we recognize distinct cell types, usually by gross histology and cytohistology, different organisms have different numbers of cell types. The numbers may be expected to be correlated with the numbers of distinct genes of an organism, or its DNA content.

In fact, for 13 organisms ranging from $E$ coli through sponges, yeast, round worms and man, the log log correlation is nearly linear with a .5 slope, (Kauffman [25]) suggesting that the number of cell types of an organism is crudely a square root type function of the quantity of its DNA. We must ask whether such a correlation, if it holds for more types of organisms, is likely to be an accident of selection or whether it reflects something basic about the number of ways a gene control system can behave as a function of the number of components of the system.

When the zygote of higher metazoans begins the process of differentiation, it differentiates into intermediate cell types which themselves branch further into different cell types. One can conceive of a system in which the initial blastula cells differentiated directly into as many cell types as the adult contains.

That, in higher metazoans, each cell type seems to differentiate directly into rather few other cell types may be expected to be a fundamental character of metazoan gene control systems. We will refer to this apparent property of metazoan gene control systems as RESTRICTED LOCAL ACCESSIBILITY.

Whatever the conditions which direct differentiation in specific ways, the outcome is reliable to a rather high degree.

Finally, gene control systems must be able successfully to evolve. Although we are becoming familiar with how enzymes might evolve to higher specificity and greater efficiency, rather less thought has been directed to how an interlocked system of genes, mRNA and proteins might successfully evolve. When we note that the cell types in a human and a shark are much the same, it is apparent that the gene control system must be so desgined that cell types can be left roughly unaltered, while the proportions and places of their occurrence in an organism change in evolution.

### 3. Homeostasis:   constrained dynamic behavior

We return to the problem of achieving restricted patterns of gene activity in organisms with perhaps thousands of genes.

As is well substantiated, (Jacob and Monod [22], Gilbert and Muller [18], [19], Ptashne [31], [32]) the rate of transcription in bacteria is controlled by inputs to an operon of specific products of other genes (eg. the repressor) and, for the operons studied, a small metabolite.

We need now to ask whether genes tend to be able to assume finely graded levels of steady activity or whether they tend to be either very active or very inactive. Both theory and experiment seem to suggest the latter to be true. First, the number of copies of many genes per cell is small, probably one or two. Graded levels of activity by having varying proportions of many genes active is impossible, and a single gene at any moment is either actively transcribing or is not. Intermediate levels of gene activity could be had, however, by time averages over periods long with respect to the time of transcription.

A second theoretical reason to think genes tend to be either highly active or nearly inactive stems from the behavior of allosteric enzymes. All known allosteric enzymes are multimeric (Monod, Changeux and Wyman [29]), a property which confers upon them the capacity for cooperative behavior (Monod, Changeux and Wyman [29]). Cooperative behavior evidences itself in sigmoid response curves to levels of substrate and allosteric inhibitors [29] (although there is some difficulty with allosteric activators [29]). Sigmoid functions can behave like threshold devices. If the sigmoid is shallow, Walters et. al [39] have shown that a sequence of sigmoids in series can behave, as a set, like a single steep sigmoid, thus providing a threshold-like, or switching, device. Finally the lac repressor is known to be a tetramer protein (Riggs [34]), and induction in vivo yields a sigmoid response curve on its inputs, (Herzenberg [21], Boezi and Cowie [8], and Bourgeois [10]).

We will therefore suppose that genes tend to be either quite active or nearly inactive; and we consider the gene control system to be the integrated system of genes, mRNA, proteins and metabolites, by which one gene's product can influence the rate of activity of other genes. We will focus attention on transcription control, and ask how genes which are nearly full on or full off can be coupled to one another so that the entire system exhibits constrained homeostatic behavior, that is, restricted patterns of gene activation, and strong tendencies to return to those patterns after many different perturbations, and how they might be coupled to achieve restricted accessibility during differentiation, the capacity to evolve, and their other global control tasks, as described in §2.

## 4. Model systems

To facilitate the discussion, we introduce several idealizations. First, the gene will be considered a binary switch, capable only of being fully on or fully off. Time will be considered to occur in discrete, clocked moments. The pathway by which the output of a gene comes to influence another gene (say by translation of a specific mRNA to a repressor molecule, or to an enzyme which catalyses the formation of a metabolite which serves as an input to the target gene) will be ignored. In another paper [24] we discuss relaxation of the idealizations to include genes whose activities can vary continuously with their inputs, consider continuous time, and consider the pathways of inter-connection between genes.

A model gene control system is a set of $N$ binary "genes" coupled together such that the outputs of genes serve as inputs which control the activity of other genes, together with a rule (boolean function) for each gene specifying how it will behave at the next integer time moment for any current set of values of its inputs.

The structure of such model gene control systems will be classified by the number of components $N$ and and the mean number of inputs per component $K$.

We distinguish three broad ways in which an input control molecule to a gene, say a repressor, might bind to the target gene.

1. The repressor might bind weakly and reversibly, so that maintainance of repression of the gene re-

quires a concentration of repressor molecules sufficient to guarantee that a new repressor binds nearly as soon as an old repressor comes off the locus.

2. The input molecule might bind firmly, and only be removed by a specific other molecule.

3. Input molecules might bind irreversibly to the target gene so that the only way an unbounded copy of the gene can be obtained is by replication.

In this paper we consider only the first of these, in [24] the latter two are discussed. They do not alter the conclusions we will reach.

## 5. One input control systems

Gene control systems of cells are almost certainly not one input systems. Indeed, in the cases which are best known, bacterial operons, the operator locus has at least two specific inputs. For example, for an inducible gene, the inputs are the repressor molecule and the inducer metabolite. Nevertheless it is useful to consider the characteristics of systems in which each component has only one input.

Perhaps the first structure which comes to mind when one begins to consider coupled nets of genes is a hierarchical, acyclic, one input system derived from a single highest member of the hierarchy. The notion was first mentioned for gene control systems by Waddington [37] who coined the phrase "cascade derepression" to describe the behavior of the system when the first gene is activated and subsequently activates its immediate descendents in the hierarchy, and so on. The notion of a cascade sequence branching downstream was taken over by Britten and Davidson [11] in their concept of a hierarchy of batteries of genes. Its attractive feature is that it allows a single input to the initial gene of the hierarchy to affect the activities of many genes, so providing a way a single

steroid molecule, for example, might have wide geno-
tropic effects.

There are two major disadvantages to one input
systems such as this. The most obvious is the lack
of reliability of the behavior of the system when
faced with component failure either due to mistakes
while running, or due to mutation of the genes involved.
There is no redundancy in the command structure. A
single mutation can disconnect all members of the
hierarchy descendent from the mutated gene. The
second disadvantage occurs in one input systems which
have structural loops. As we shall see in detail below,
such systems do not behave in very restricted ways,
and exhibit rather little homeostatic tendency to
return to a mode of behavior once perturbed.

## 6. Multiple input control systems

Cellular gene control systems appear to have more
than one input per gene, and, noting the feedback
loops in repression and enzyme inhibition, are not
acyclic structure. The possibility of many inputs per
element allows the possibility of redundancy, and
thus more reliable behavior. Furthermore, in general,
the greater the number of inputs to elements of a
system, the more subtle and complex can be the
system's behavior. However these advantages are
bought for a price. As we shall show below, systems
with many inputs per element do not usually show
highly restricted patterns of activity, nor strongly
homeostatic properties. To obtain constrained, homeostatic behavior requires increasingly subtle construction as the number of inputs per element increases.

One of the most obvious ways to obtain homeostatic
behavior is to build multi-input systems which have
many forcing structures in them. Indeed, as we shall
see it now begins to appear that perhaps the *only* way

to build large nets of switching elements which exhibit homeostasis and the other biologically "good" global behaviors noted in §2, without highly orderly construction of the interconnections between genes, is to build systems either rich in extended forcing structures or at least rich in components which are forcible on one or more input lines.

## 7. Forcing structures in switching nets

Elements in a switching net realize boolean functions on their inputs. A boolean function is a rule which prescribes for an element with $K$ inputs what its value (0 or 1) shall be at time $T + 1$, for each of the $2^K$ possible sets of values of its $K$ inputs at time $T$. Consider an element which receives two inputs, and switches on at $T + 1$ if and only if either the first, or the second, or both input lines carried a 1 value at time $T$. The element realizes the OR function. An element will be said to be *forcible* on a given input line, if *one* of the two possible values of the input line causes the element to assume *one* of its two values at the next time moment, *regardless* of the values on any of the remaining input lines. We restrict the definition to elements with more than one input. For example, an element realizing the OR function is forcible on *both* its input lines, since a 1 value on either input line forces the element to assume the value 1 at the next time moment regardless of the value on the other input line. The FORCED VALUE of an element is that value to which it is forcible. An element realizing an OR function has a forced value of 1. An element realizing the function EXCLUSIVE OR switches on at $T + 1$ if and only if, at $T$, either its first input was on and the second was off, or the second was on and the first was off. If both were simultaneously on, or off, the element switches to 0 at $T + 1$. An element realizing the

EXCLUSIVE OR function is not forcible on either input line, for no value on either input line guarantees that the element will be 0, or 1, the next time moment, regardless of the value of the other input line.

If an element $A$ is an input to element $B$, $A$ will be said to *force* $B$ if and only if:

1. $A$ is itself forcible on at least one of its own input lines.

2. $B$ is forcible on the input line from $A$.

3. The FORCED VALUE of $A$ is the value of $A$ which forces $B$ to its forced value. For example, suppose $A$ has two inputs and realizes an OR function on them; and let $B$ have two inputs, of which one is $A$, and realize an OR function on them. Then $A$ forces $B$ because $A$ is itself forcible on at least one input; $B$ is forcible on the input line from $A$; and the forced value of $A$, 1, is the value of the input line from $A$ to $B$ which forces $B$ to its forced value. However, if $A$ has realized the AND function, then its forced value would have been 0, not 1, which is not the value of the input line from $A$ to $B$ that forces $B$, and $A$ would not have forced $B$.

So defined, the relation between elements of FORCING is a transitive, and nonsymmetric relation. If $A$ forces $B$ and $B$ forces $C$, then $A$ forces $C$ with a delay of 2 time moments. That $A$ forces $B$ does not imply that $B$ forces $A$. However, since $A$ can be an input to itself, and force itself, the relationship of forcing can be reflexive.

In order to apply the concept of forcing to switching nets, we need two simple theorems and some concepts from graph theory.

1B. *If an element $A$ is forcible on more than one input line, then its* FORCED VALUE *is identical for all the lines on which it is forcible.*

1A. *For an element with $M$ inputs, the maximum*

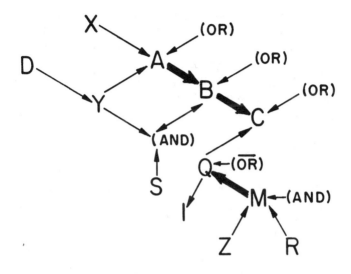

FIGURE 1. Heavy arrows represent forcing inputs, light arrows are nonforcing inputs, in a switching net.

*number of forcing inputs is* $M$.[1] *The minimum is* 0.

A directed graph is a set of points, a set of arrows, and two rules. The first rule assigns the tail of each arrow to a particular point; the second rule assigns the head of each arrow to some particular point. A SUBGRAPH is a subset of the points and arrows of the initial graph, connected as they were in the initial graph.

We may consider each gene in a model genetic switching net as a point, and the input lines as incoming arrows, hence representing the net by a graph. Making use of our definition of forcing function, we may examine the boolean function realized by each gene on its inputs, and create a subgraph of the switching net by keeping only those connections which are forcing. This FORCING GRAPH of the switching net

---

[1] See Appendix 1, Theorem 1A and 1B.

is a subgraph embedded in the entire switching net; in it an arrow from $A$ to $B$ means that $A$ forces $B$ in the initial switching net's behavior. (Figure 1).

We define the FORCING STRUCTURE OF AN ELEMENT to be (1) the set of all elements of the forcing graph which that element can reach by directed paths (i.e. by following arrows tail to head sequentially), plus (2) the set of all elements which can reach that element by directed paths. The forcing structure of an element is its descendent tree plus its antecedent tree, those elements which directly or indirectly it forces, or force it.

An element may be a member of its own forcing structure; if so, then the element lies on a FORCING LOOP or FORCING CYCLE such that it is its own predecessor and successor. We now investigate the properties of forcing loops.

Consider a forcing loop in a switching net of many components, in which $A$ forces $B$, $B$ forces $C$, and $C$ forces $A$, and where each receives other nonforcing inputs (see Figure 2). By the definition of forcing, if $A$ is currently in its forced value, $B$ must assume its forced value one moment later, regardless of what $B$'s other inputs are doing. Thus, if $A$ is currently in its forced value, then a forced value propagates around the three element forcing loop in three time moments. No values of any inputs in the switching net arriving at $A$, $B$ or $C$, can dislodge the forced value from propagating around the loop. On the other hand, new forced values can enter the loop at loci not currently forced. When $A$ is not currently in its forced value, then $B$'s behavior the next time moment depends not only on $A$'s value, but on its remaining inputs. If these values happen to cause $B$ to assume $B$'s forced value, a new forced value enters the forcing loop and cannot thereafter be dislodged. Eventually, every available locus

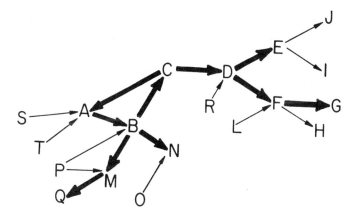

FIGURE 2. A 3 element forcing loop, *A*, *B*, *C*, with descendent forcing tree.

in the forced loop will be expected to become filled with a forced value, and thereafter the behavior of the loop will be fixed at a steady state in which each element remains at its forced value. Every gene in the forcing loop may send forcing arrows to genes not on the loop. This entire descendent forcing structure will also eventually be forced to the appropriate forced values and remain fixed in one state.

We now define the STRONG FORCING structure of a component *j* to be all those elements which *j* both forces (directly or indirectly) and which also force *j*. The strong forcing structure of an element *j* is all those elements, including *j*, which can mutually reach each other by forcing paths. Consider the subgraph of a genetic net's forcing graph which is a given component's strong forcing structure *S*. We may form a new graph $S^2$ by connecting each point in *S* with all those points that it can reach in *S* by paths length 2. Similarly, we may form a new graph $S^3$ by joining each point with those points which in *S* it can reach by forcing paths length 3. Suppose for some integer *R*, $S^R$, each is a completely connected graph, that is, in $S^R$, each point can reach each point by a single arrow. If this condition obtains $S$, the strong forcing structure of an element $j$ will be said to be BEHAVIORALLY ACYCLIC, or to be REGULAR. If, at time $T$, any member of the strong forcing structure is in its forced value, then $R$ moments later that forced value will simultaneously arrive at all members of $S$, and all members of $S$ will be fixed thereafter at their forced value.

With a finite delay, after the introduction of a single forced value into an acyclic forcing structure, all members of that structure and their descendent forcing structures will be forced.

Obviously forcing loops constrain the behavior of a switching system powerfully and exhibit a strong homeostatic tendency to return to the state with all elements forced, if ever perturbed.

Three interrelated factors tend to constrain dynamic behavior in forcing structures which have no loops–that is, unilaterally connected forcing structures. Consider a straight chain, in which $A$ forces $B$, $B$ forces $C$, etc., and let this forcing structure from a model genetic switching net have nonforcing inputs to its members from elsewhere in the genetic net. As in the forcing loop, by definition of forcing, once a forced value enters this straight forcing chain at any point, it cannot leave except by propagating until it reaches the last member of the forcing chain, and passes off. But forcing values can enter at any element on the chain whose forcing input is not currently in its forced value. This creates a strong tendency for the later members of the chain to be in their forced value most or all of the time.

This effect is enhanced if, instead of a straight chain, the ancestor tree to any element is well branched, for the chance that an element is currently forced is the appropriate sum of the chances that each of its predecessors was forced at the right moment previously.

Finally, consider an acyclic forcing structure in which $A$ reaches $B$ by several directed paths. Let there be a path length 1 from $A$ to $B$, a path length 2, another length 3, and so on up to a path length $K$. Then if $A$ is currently in its forced value, $B$ will be forced for $K$ consecutive moments. For a rather extensive acyclic forcing structure rich in such directed semicycles, later members of the structure will be forced most of the time.

## 8. The size of forcing structures as a function of the number of inputs per element in model genetic control nets

The extent to which behavior in a switching net is constrained by forcing structures depends upon the size and extent of those structures spreading throughout the net. The number of possible boolean functions a switching element with $K$ inputs might realize is $2^{2^K}$. The fraction of these which are forcible on one or more input lines is maximum when $K = 2$; 14 of the 16 functions are forcible. As $K$ grows large, the subset of forcible boolean functions grows much smaller. If boolean functions are assigned to elements from the entire $2^{2^K}$ possible functions, we show in Appendix 1 that the expected number of actual *forcing* connections $R$ in a net of $N$ elements is less than

$$R < NK/2 \cdot$$

$$\left[ 2^{K+1}(K + \sum_{I=0}^{K-2} (2^{2^I} - 1)\,(K - I)\,(K - I - 1)) \right]^2 \Big/ 2^{2^K}$$

which grows very small for more than 3 inputs per element. Forcing structures will be largest in nets with 2 inputs per element, if all possible boolean functions may be used.

However, nets with many inputs per element rich in forcing structures may be built by utilizing only forcible boolean functions from the increasingly improbable subset of such functions as $K$ increases.

We now consider systems constructed without careful selection from restricted subsets of boolean functions, in order to evaluate the effect of the average number of inputs per element, and the number of elements in the net, on the global properties of the system's behavior [25].

## 9. Behavior as a function of the size of a model genetic control system, and the number of control inputs per model gene

These model genetic nets are constructed by choosing a value of $N$ the number of elements in the net, and of $K$, the number of input lines to any gene. Each gene receives exactly $K$ inputs, one from each of $K$ model genes among the $N$. Nets are randomly constructed in two distinct senses, the $K$ inputs to each gene are chosen randomly; to each gene one of the $2^{2^K}$ boolean functions of $K$ inputs is assigned randomly. After construction, the structure of the nets is fixed. We assume all genes compute one step in one clocked time moment. The behavior of such systems was explored by computer simulation.

A STATE of the net is a list of the present value of each gene. Since each element can be on or off, there are $2^N$ possible states.

If the system is placed in some state at time $T$, at $T + 1$, each gene scans the present value of each of its inputs, consults its boolean function and assumes the value specified by the function for that input configuration. The net passes from a state to only one subsequent state. There are a finite number of states. As the system passes along a sequence of states

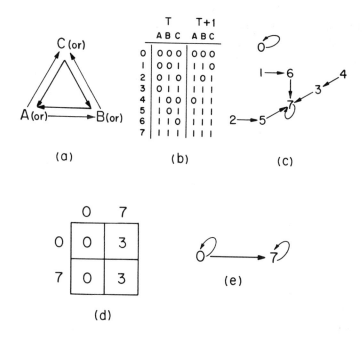

FIGURE 3. (a) Switching net in which each element has inputs from the other two, and realizes an OR function on its inputs. (b) Functions realized by *A, B* and *C* on their inputs, as derived from 4a. Each row is a state of the net. States are numbered 0-7. (c) Kinetograph showing state transitions from 4b. There are two state cycles, each one state long. (d) Flow matrix for the two state cycles for all possible reversals to one element's activity. All three perturbations cause state cycle 0 to go to state cycle 7. No perturbation causes state cycle 7 to go to state cycle 0. (e) Flow among cycles without, and with, slight perturbations.

from any arbitrarily chosen initial state, it must eventually re-enter a state previously passed. Thereafter, the system cycles continuously through the re-entered sequence of states, called a STATE CYCLE, whose length is the number of states on the cycle. (Figure 3).

A model genetic net must have at least one state cycle, but may have more. The number of state cycles is the number of distinct different ways the system can behave.

PERTURBATION. As a net passes around a state cycle, one unit of perturbation may be introduced by arbitrarily changing the value of a single gene, then releasing the system. After perturbation, the system may return to the state cycle from which it was perturbed, or run to another cycle. By perturbing all states on each state cycle in all possible ways, one gene at a time, a matrix may be obtained listing the total number of times the system returned to the state cycle perturbed, or ran to, each other cycle. Dividing the value in each cell of this matrix by its row total yields the corresponding matrix of transition probabilities between state cycles under the drive of random, one unit, perturbation. This transition probability matrix will be called the FLOW MATRIX among the state cycles.

TOTALLY CONNECTED NETS, $K = N$. When $N$ is large, and $K = N$, so that each gene has an input from every gene, the density of forcible functions is very low, so $R$ is very small, and nets have almost no forcing structures. Behavior would not be expected to be localized, nor to show homeostatic return to a localized subset of states after small perturbation. In these nets, the expected state cycle length is $2^{N/2}$, the square root of the number of states. With only 2000 genes, such a system would cycle through $2^{1000} \approx 10^{300}$ states. Although state cycles are very long, $K = N$ nets exhibit a very important characteristic: the expected number of distinct cycles is only $(1/e)N$, a linear function of $N$. This strong constraint will assume greater importance later on. $K = N$ nets show very little or no homeostatic tendency to return to the cycle from which they were perturbed. Further, a single unit perturbation can take the system from nearly any of its $(1/e)N$ cycles to any other one. That is, these systems also do not show restricted local reachability.

$K = 1$ NETS. We saw that real genetic control systems were almost certainly not one input systems. One input nets have no forcing structures, by the definition of forcing. Such a net falls apart into separate cyclic structures, and state cycles are roughly the lowest common multiple of the structural loop lengths. Cycle lengths are very long, the number of state cycles is huge–about

$$\left( \frac{2^{N/\ln(N)}}{2(N/\ln(N))} \right)^{\ln(N)} {}_{2)}$$

One input systems show almost no homeostatic return to a state cycle which is perturbed, and each cycle can reach approximately $N$ other state cycles by a single perturbation, and can reach all possible state cycles by a sequence of single perturbations. That is, one input systems do not show restricted local reachability.

$K = 2$ NETS. The density of elements forcible on one or more input lines, or actual extended forcing structures is high in $K = 2$ nets. The behavior of typical nets is highly localized, exhibits marked homeostatic return to a perturbed cycle, and marked restricted local reachability. State cycle lengths are typically only square root $N$. A net with 10,000 genes and $2^{10,000} = 10^{3000}$ states cycles repeatedly through a minuscule 100 states. The number of state cycles is also very few,

---

[2] The one input net state cycle analysis is in the Journal of Cybernetics, Vol. 1, Issue 1, S. Kauffman, Spring 1971, in press.

only square root $N$. This result is particularly important. Further, the system exhibits strong homeostatic properties, returning to the cycle perturbed for about .9 to .95 of the possible unit perturbations. Finally, $K = 2$ nets also show marked restricted local reachability, for even if the number of state cycles is, say, 50, perturbation can cause a single cycle to flow to only about 5 or 6 other cycles. That is, the FLOW MATRIX of a $K = 2$ net has mostly 0 entries.

### $K = 2$ nets built with neither forcible elements nor extended forcing structures

Among the 16 boolean functions of 2 inputs, two are not forcible on either input. These functions are EXCLUSIVE OR, and IF AND ONLY IF. Nets built using exclusively these two functions have neither forcible elements nor forcing structures and have enormously long state cycles (Walker [38]). The expected number of cycles in such nets is not known.

### $K = 2$ nets built *with* many forcible elements, but without extended forcing structures

An element realizing the AND function is forcible on both inputs to 0, an element realizing an OR function is forcible on both inputs to 1. However if an element realizing AND on its inputs is an input to an element realizing an OR function, the "AND" element does not actually force the OR element, since the forced value of the "AND" element, 0, is not the value which forces the "OR" to its forced value 1. Preliminary results suggest that two input nets built with many elements that are forcible on both inputs, but with the actual number of forcing connections $R$ small (from $.2N$ to $.5N$), have short state cycles roughly like randomly built $K = 2$ nets rich in extended forcing structures.

When $R$ is $.5N$ or less, we show in §11 that the net will contain few extended forcing structures. This result, coupled with studies on nets with extensive forcing structures, suggests that extensive forcing structures may be a sufficient but not necessary condition for the occurrance of short state cycles. Further, the presence of very many forcible components by itself seems to be sufficient to guarantee reasonably short state cycles.

These nets also seem to have about square root $N$ state cycles. The character of their flow matrices is unknown.

$K = 3$ NETS. Nets with 3 inputs per element, where the boolean function of each element is chosen at random from the 256 possible functions, have state cycles which become too long to be found by computer simulation search through 10,000 states when $N$ is greater than 100. However, if the restricted set of boolean functions of 3 inputs which are forcible on one, two or all three inputs, are used to generate model nets, such nets behave as do nets with 2 inputs per element.

These computer simulations suggest a very strong conclusion. When $K = N$, the number of state cycles is only $(1/e)N$. When $K = 2$ or 3, the number of state cycles is square root $N$. Thus the number of state cycles, as a function of $K$, only increases from a square root function to a linear function of $N$ as $K$ goes from 2 to $N$. These results suggest that when the number of inputs $K$ is small almost any switching net will have about square root $N$ modes of behavior, and certainly almost any net rich in forcing structures will have about $N^{1/2}$ modes of behavior unless it is constructed in rather particular ways. Furthermore, any

net rich in forcing structures should show strong
homeostatic properties, and strongly restricted local
reachability, unless constructed in an odd way.

The properties of forcing structures developed in §7
led us to think that most members of an acyclic forcing
structure would be fixed in their forced values, and
that all members of forcing loops and their descendent
trees would be fixed in their forced values. Results
with $K = 2$ nets suggest this is true. On any state
cycle in such a net usually about .7-.8 of elements are
fixed at a constant value, the remainder oscillate
between being active and inactive. Generally, about
.6-.7 of the elements are fixed at the same value, 0
or 1, on *all* the state cycles of which the net is capable.
In $K = 2$ nets rich in forcible elements, but constructed
without extended forcing structures, although state
cycles are short, only about $.15N$ to $.25N$ of the elements are fixed in value on one state cycle. Even
fewer are fixed on all state cycles.

We now briefly describe the behavior of hierarchically
constructed nets in which each element receives $K = 2$
inputs, but in which some genes may serve as input to
very many genes, and other genes may serve as inputs
to none. The mean number of outputs per gene is also $K$.
Such systems behave exactly like nonhierarchical $K = 2$
nets, but with fewer elements. The cycle lengths and
number of cycles of hierarchical nets are roughly square
root functions of the EFFECTIVE $N$, where

$$N_e = \frac{N}{1 + \mathrm{Var}_K/\overline{\overline{K}}}$$

when $\mathrm{Var}_K$ is the variance in the number of outputs
per element, and $\overline{K}$ the mean number of outputs.

## 10. Biological implications[3]

In §2 we mentioned several global characteristics of the behavior of real genetic control systems which must be explained: Patterns of gene activity are highly constrained relative to the potential range of variability in gene activity, cells exhibit marked homeostatic properties, any metazoan cell type differentiates directly into only rather few other cell types (restricted local accessability), there is a strong correlation between the amount of DNA in an organism's cells and the number of its cell types, and the gene control system must be able to evolve successfully. We now show that model genetic nets rich in forcing structures behave in ways which could account for these properties.

A. CELL CYCLE TIME. There is a strong correlation between the amount of DNA per cell, and cell cycle time. In fact, the mean cell cycle time in minutes is about a square root function of the DNA per cell of the organism. Model nets with 2 inputs per element, or those with 3 or 4 inputs which utilize only forcible functions, have state cycles whose length increases at about a square root function of the number of elements of the net. Thus the time required for a switching net to traverse its state cycle is about a square root function of the number of elements in the net, which parallels the biologic data.

B. NUMBER OF CELL TYPES. A strong result of computer studies of switching nets is that almost any model genetic control system with large forcing structures, particularly with two or three inputs per element, will have about square root $N$ distinct state cycles,

---

[3] More extensive discussion of biological implications of the theory may be found in [26].

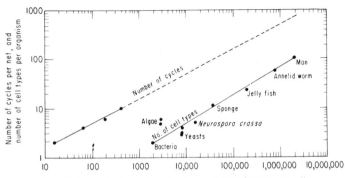

No. of elements in the random net and estimated no. of genes per cell

FIGURE 4. Log number of cell types plotted against log estimated number of genes. The theoretical curve shows log number of state cycles against log $N$.

each a different permanent way the model genetic system can behave. Let us, for the moment, suppose that each state cycle of a model genetic control system corresponds to a distinct cell type of which the model control system is capable. Then the theory makes the strong prediction that the number of cell types in an organism ought to be roughly a square root function of its number of genes. In Figure 4 we plot the logarithm of the number of cell types of various organisms as classified by gross histology and sometimes cyto-histological techniques, against the logarithm of the estimated number of genes in the organism. The number of genes was estimated by assuming the $E$ coli has about 2000 genes, and taking linear proportions for cells with more DNA than $E$ coli. The data lie roughly on a straight line for 13 organisms. Its slope, like that of the number of state cycles as a function of $N$, is .5, a square root type slope in a log log plot. Thus, at face value, the model seems rather strikingly to give some information as to the rate at which the number of cell types in organisms increases as a function of the quantity of DNA per cell. Further evaluation of this hypothesis is given in [26].

C. THE FLOW MATRIX: HOMEOSTASIS AND RESTRICTED PATHWAYS OF DIFFERENTIATION. If state cycles, the stable modes of behavior of a model gene net, correspond to cell types, then flows between state cycles model differentiation. As we noted in §2 there is considerable evidence in higher metazoans that each cell type differentiates directly to at most rather few other cell types, which may themselves branch to further cell types. Furthermore, there is evidence suggesting that a given cell type, perturbed with a wide variety of stimuli, can still only differentiate directly into one of a few cell types. The strongest evidence for this lies in the long story of neural induction, in which it has become clear that very many agents can induce the presumptive neural tissue to differentiate into neural tissue. This might be due to the fact that all the diverse agents act on the same point in the system, causing the same result, but it is surely more plausible to think that the presumptive neural tissue is poised, as it were, and nearly any stimuli, acting on diverse points in the system, will push it into being neural tissue.

As we noted, switching nets with 2 or 3 inputs per component exhibit precisely these properties under the drive of random, small perturbations. Any mode of behavior is returned to after reversal of the value of a randomly chosen gene with a probability of about .9. If perturbations can cause the system to move away from one state cycle, they can only cause it to move to a few, say five or six, other state cycles. Thus the systems exhibit both marked homeostasis and marked restricted local reachability. It may be noted that, in general, the transition probabilities between two state cycles are not symmetric; usually it is easier to go from one to the other than back. In addition, these nets often exhibit RESTRICTED GLOBAL ACCESSIBILITY, that is, at least some state cycles are unable to reach all the other state cycles (through intermediate state cycles) by sequences of perturbations to one gene's activity at a time.

Hadorn [20] and others have studied the "stability" of the "determined" state of imaginal disks of Drosophila larva by culturing specific disks, for example the wing disk, in the abdomen of an adult fly from some number of generations of transfer from adult abdomen to adult abdomen, then transplanted the progeny of the disk tissue back into a larva undergoing metamorphosis to see if the tissue would give rise to that structure for which it was initially determined. Generally such homotypic development occurs. However, occasionally, tissue from one disk becomes "transdetermined" and gives rise to a structure deriving normally from a different imaginal disk.

Several characteristics of the flow pathways of such transdeterminations are of interest to the present discussion (Figure 5). Hadorn et. al. have now found several structures which transdetermine one to another. In general, the time of occurrence of a given transdetermination seems to be random, but to occur with roughly constant probability per transfer generation. Usually the probability of transdetermination from one structure to a second is not identical with the reverse probability. Each structure can only transdetermine into two or three others directly, and there are some structures which cannot reach all other structures by transdetermination. For example, all structures can directly or indirectly transdetermine into mesothorax,

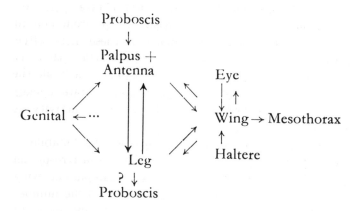

FIGURE 5. Transdetermination pathways in *Drosophila*
after Gehring [17].

but mesothorax has never been found to transdetermine
into any other structure.

D. CAPACITY TO EVOLVE. A great deal of evolution
seems to have kept cell types much the same, but
altered the circumstances of their occurrence, the
structures built of them, and the proportions of
different cell types utilized in the different organisms.
In short, the construction of the genetic control net
must allow alterations of genes which largely leave
cell types unaltered, but which change the conditions
under which those cell types will occur.

It is an obvious, but important, point that not every
conceivable gene control system can operate this way.
For example, if a gene control system were a net of
switches each of which had inputs from very many other
genes and the boolean functions were assigned completely
randomly from among all possible functions of those
numerous inputs, then mutation of any gene to produce
a useless product would be expected to alter every state
cycle of the system, that is, to alter every "cell type".

On the other hand, systems with few inputs per element can be altered by mutation in such a way that all state cycles are left unchanged, and only the stimuli which cause the system to flow between the state cycles are altered. Nets with two inputs per element have short state cycles because many elements of the forcing structures fall to their forced value and remain fixed there. Suppose there is a gene $i$ which is inactive on all state cycles of the system. If that element is removed from the net–or switched permanently off by a mutation which renders its output useless–that removal will not alter any state cycle of the system. Symmetrically, if an element $j$ is active on all state cycles, its mutation to a "constitutive" state will not alter any state cycle of the system.

Such mutations however *do* alter which states run into which state cycles. The consequence is that, although the state cycles of the nonmutant system are left unaltered, the transition probabilities of flow among the cycles by perturbation may be changed. If modes are cell types, such a mutation alters the flow among cell types, but not the cell types.

The same effect may be obtained by adding a new gene $m$ to the system and giving it a forcing repressing input from a member of the net which is always active on all state cycles. Then $m$ will be inactive on all those state cycles, and the cycles will be unaltered. However, if its repressive input is transiently inhibited, $m$ can be active and lead to new behavior, either to a flow to another old state cycle, or to a newly created state cycle. In short, old modes of behavior may be kept while new ones are added and flows are altered.

Clearly the capacity to do these things rests on the occurrence of elements which are constantly active or constantly inactive on all state cycles–i.e. on all cell types. Systems with forcing structures seem most likely to have these properties. Such a system is obviously highly desirable, for it partially uncouples the cell type from the conditions of its occurrence. If favorable cell types are found in evolution, they can be kept, and utilized in diverse circumstances.

We note that nets rich in forcible elements, but without extended forcing structures have only about $.2N$ elements fixed on all state cycles. It would be harder for such systems to evolve without altering state cycles than nets rich in forcing structures where about $.5N$ to $.6N$ elements are fixed on all state cycles.

The effects of mutation of a gene normally fixed off, or on to one irreversibily off or on, has been studied by computer simulations on nets with 50 elements and 2 inputs per element. If a net has $L$ state cycles, then each state cycle can conceivably flow by perturbation to $L$ state cycles. The FLOW MATRIX is an $L \times L$ matrix. Let $M$ be the number of elements in a net which are either fixed off on all state cycles, or fixed on. The effects of irreversible "mutation" of an element to its behaviorally fixed state was examined by trying all $M$ mutations, one at a time, and examining the corresponding FLOW matrix for each mutant net. Two general results emerge: (1) any single mutation of this type tends to affect from none to about one third of the $L^2$ flows among the $L$ state cycles, (2) some flows are far more resistant to alteration by mutation of any one of the $M$ than are others. The first would be important in the capacity to evolve in specific ways, the second might play a role in the canalization of behavior of a genetic control system (Rendel [33], Fraser [16]).

The discussion of this section leads us to distinguish between what might be called DEVELOPMENTAL genes, and CELL TYPE genes, in organisms. That is, there are likely to exist in organisms genes which are either normally inactive on all cell types, or active on all cell types. Mutation of these to and from constitutively active or inactive states would be expected to alter differentiation among cell types, but not the cell types themselves.

## 11. Expected character of forcing structures as a function of the number of forcing connections

We have seen that homeostatic behavior and other global behaviors which seem to fit many global features of cellular gene control systems occur in switching nets with few inputs per component, and rich in forcing structures which constrain their behavior. Let $R$ be the number of forcing connections in a net of $N$ components. We now examine the kinds of forcing structure to be expected as a function of $R$ relative to $N$ under random construction rules. Selection may or may not have wielded possible real forcing connections in real genetic systems into highly improbable structures. Our examination will give a background for further evaluation.

We define a WEAK FORCING STRUCTURE to be a set of genes each of which is connected to at least one other member of the set by a forcing arrow, but with no regard for the direction of the arrow.

From Erdös and Renyi's work [15] on random graphs, when $R$ is very small relative to $N$, the switching net contains very many very small weak forcing trees. When $R = N/2$, a threshold has been reached and most of the small weak forcing trees have grown together into one giant weak forcing structure, with a few small separate forcing trees.

A second reason why behavior becomes constrained as $R$ approaches $N$ is that $R = N$ appears to be a second threshold at which *directed* forcing loops become plentiful.

We saw above that such forcing loops would be expected to fall to a steady state with all elements at their forced value, and subsequently all members of the loop's descendent forcing tree would fall to fixed state.

Where $\alpha = R/N$, and when $R$ is reasonably less than $N$, we can show (Appendix 2) that the expected number of elements on forcing loops is $\approx 2\alpha/1 - \alpha$, and that an upper bound on the expected number of elements on forcing loops, or descendent from each loop element is $2\alpha/1 - 2\alpha + \alpha^2$. By Monte Carlo computer technique, $N = 100$ and for $R$ from about $.95N$ to about $1.4N$, the size of the strong forcing component (i.e. interconnected forcing loops) in a switching net was nearly constant at about $.25N$. Another $.25N$ components were descendents of this strong, interconnected set of forcing loops. Preliminary simulations suggest the behavior of switching nets with $R = .9N$ and $R = 1.5N$ are qualitatively very similar.

For $K = 2$ nets, $R \approx .9N$; while for $K = 3$ $R \approx .5N$ and for $K = 4$ $R \approx .004N$. Thus only randomly built $K = 2$ nets have large forcing structures. With more inputs per element, forcible boolean functions must be chosen from among the many nonforcible functions.

Thus in switching nets with few inputs per component and rich in forcing connections, we may expect one huge weak forcing structure extending like a reticulum throughout the net, several small separate weak forcing structures, and, embedded as a subgraph within the huge weak forcing structure, an interconnected set of strong directed forcing loops plus their descendent forced tree. If real genetic control systems achieve their global behaviors due to the occurrence in them of forcing structures, these results allow us an educated guess as to the global construction of these forcing structures.

## 12. Control advantages of forcing structures

In §5 we discussed one input control systems. The advantage, with a hierarchically ordered descendent branching tree, is that a single input, like a hormone, to the highest gene in the tree can control the activities of the many genes in the cascade below it. The two major disadvantages were: (1) the lack of control redundancy, so that any single mutation could disconnect all genes below the mutation from higher control; (2) also, one input control systems with structural loops behave on long state cycles, have many state cycles, and show neither much homeostasis nor restricted local reachability.

By contrast, an extended forcing structure maintains the control advantages of a one input system but overcomes the disadvantages. In a large forcing structure, any component, placed in its forced value, determines uniquely the subsequent states of the members of its descendent forcing structure. Hence, input to such a gene by, say, a steroid, which put that gene into its forced value, could uniquely determine the activities of many genes. Unlike one input systems, only one value, 1 or 0, of a member of a forcing structure propagates uniquely.

Since a gene which is forcible on more than one input line is always forcible to the same forced value on all those lines, forcing structures allow, and commonly have, redundancy of control. A forcing value on any input line forces the element to the same binary value. Loss of one input line by mutation need not greatly alter the system's behavior. Forcing structures, particularly with structural loops, behave homeostatically.

By contrast, nets rich in forcible elements, but constructed without extended forcing structures, do not maintain these control advantages, even though they do have short, and few, state cycles.

## 13. Molecular mechanisms

If molecular mechanisms which could realize forcible functions, and so generate forcing structures, were hard for organisms to build, it would be correspondingly difficult to imagine that gene control systems are rich in extended forcing structures. It seems to be relatively easy, however, to build molecules which realize functions forcible on one or more control inputs, and might be rather harder to build molecular mechanisms which at the same time can be reliably controlled to be nearly off or nearly on, and which realize nonforcible functions.

Consider a hypothetical allosteric enzyme (or repressor molecule) with one kind of allosteric site. Suppose that site binds two input metabolites, $A$ and $B$, and both cause the enzyme (repressor) to be active. Then it is easy to suppose that if $A$ alone causes the enzyme to be active, and so does $B$ alone, then in the presence of both $A$ and $B$, whichever binds to the allosteric sites, the enzyme will be active. In this simple case, the enzyme realizes the OR function on its inputs, and can be forced by either input to be active regardless of the presence of the other input. On the other hand, suppose the enzyme is to realize the nonforcible function, EXCLUSIVE OR, where it is activated by $A$ alone, or $B$ alone, but not both. It is hard to imagine this occuring; it requires that either $A$ or $B$ when alone activates the enzyme by binding to the allosteric sites, but that both jointly present fail to do so.

## 14. "Microscopic" evidence for the theory

A. FORCIBLE OPERONS. The by now classical bacterial operons supply the most direct evidence that genes actually realize forcible functions on their control inputs in real cellular gene control systems. Consider a typical inducible enzyme such as Beta galactosidase. A repressor protein (Riggs et. al., [34]) binds, apparently fairly firmly, to the operator locus. A metabolic input, lactose, specifically removes the repressor, and allows transcription. The operon is forcible to the active state by both inputs, for if the regulator gene making the repressor is inactive, then the operon is active; if the metabolite is present, the operon is active. As noted for forcible functions multiple forcing inputs must force it to the same forced value. Here both forcible input lines force the operon to the same forced value–active, neither input alone can guarantee that the operon is inactive. The operon is only forcible to one value, not both, as we showed to be characteristic of forcible functions.

The same considerations apply to a repressible operon with its apo-repressor and co-repressor. Each, by being absent, can force the operon to be active, neither can alone force it to be inactive.

There appears to be considerable evidence that allosteric enzymes can realize forcible functions on their inputs. In at least three places where several important end products are branches in a reaction sequence of intermediate metabolism, the joint action of two or more of the end products is necessary to inhibit the activity of enzymes concerned with the common path. Such multivalent repression (Cohen [13]) of aspartokinase I and homoserine dehydrogenase I, each by the pair threonine + isoleucine, has been well established. Further, valine, leucine, isoleucine and pantothenate are all required to repress the enzymes in the biosynthetic pathways leading to valine and isoleucine [13]. In all of these cases, the enzyme realizes a forcible function, for any input can force the enzyme to be active by being itself absent.

B. NUMBER OF INPUTS PER GENE. As we have noted, bacterial operons seem to have two highly specific inputs, protein and metabolite, although other metabolites may have some influence on the operon in physiological circumstances. Equivalent data for metazoans is not available, but it seems unlikely that any gene has very many direct inputs.

C. EXTENDED FORCING STRUCTURES. We stress that while several operons appear to realize functions which are *forcible* by one or more single control inputs, this does not yet constitute evidence that any gene $i$ forces gene $j$. The binary relation "element $i$ forces element $j$" requires that $i$ itself be forcible, and that its forced value force $j$ to $j$'s forced value. The evidence is presented to show genes *do* realize forcible functions. As we showed before, nets with many forcible elements, even without extended forcing structures, have short and few state cycles. Extended forcing structures, however, appear necessary to control reliably the activity of many genes by input to one gene. We suggest that the occurrence of extended forcing structures is most likely to play a role in higher metazoans, whose cells face a stable environment, and where cell differentiation demands the stable occurrence of quite different patterns of many genes' activities, controlled by hormone, or hormone-like inputs to one or a few genes.

There is no direct evidence supporting the predicted existence of extended connected forcing structures. However, discovery of such structures is experimentally feasible. Such a structure would be characterized by a set of genetic loci each of which had more than one control input, yet which behaved in such a way that a given activity (or inactivity) of some component would propagate a specific pattern of activity and inactivity to several other loci of the set, regardless of the behavior of the remaining inputs to those other loci. The reverse activity of the first component would not propagate in a repeatable way to the remaining loci regardless of the behavior of other inputs. Specific sequences of puffing in dipteran giant chromosomes, induced by ecdysone, might be examples of extended forcing structures, but such a conclusion is far from established (Clever [12], Ashburner [3], [4], [5], Berendes [6], [7]).

## 15. Alternative theories

We wish to emphasize two alternative, or at least complementary, ways an integrated gene control system might achieve its orderly global behaviors. We defined the concept of forcible elements and of a forcing structure earlier, and showed systems rich in such components and structures behaving with bio-logic-like global order. If the gene can usefully be modeled as a binary switching device, we may ask if forcible elements are necessary to obtain "good" global behavior.

One can build large switching nets without forcible elements or extended forcing structures which have quite localized behavior, but not really orderly enough, I think, for biological systems. Consider a binary gene with many $K$ inputs. There are $2^K$ possible states of its inputs. We might assign the element a boolean function which assumed the value 1 for 75% of those $2^K$ input states, and 0 for only 25%. Consider a net built of such biased elements. There will be a marked constraint on sequences of states to converge toward the region of state space where each element is in value 1. Where $K = N$, and boolean functions are chosen at random without such bias, state cycle lengths are the square root of the number of states, and the number of distinct state cycles is $(1/e)N$. In those unbiased nets, there is little convergence in state space. With strongly biased components, 75:25, we would expect far fewer distinct state cycles and much shorter state cycles. Nevertheless, boolean functions of many inputs which yield 1 on 75 % of the input states may easily be chosen that are not forcible on any input line at all. Such nets would show constrained behavior, but contain no forcing structures, nor forcible elements.

The number of state cycles in such nets is unknown, but probably approaches square root $N$. However, state cycles, while very short with respect to the state space, are far too long to be biologically meaningful. Monte Carlo study of such nets reveals that cycle lengths are $.0005(N^4)$ which becomes enormously long for $N = 1000$. Increasing the bias of the functions appears unlikely to help as $N$ grows reasonably large. In addition to having long cycles, such systems would not be likely to show restricted local accessibility among cycles under perturbation. Further, lacking forcing structures, no single gene's behavior could uniquely determine the subsequent activity of a down-stream tree of genes. It is difficult to see how hormone or other signals would work reliably.

We conclude that, at this point, it has begun to appear that the way truly large nets of switching elements are likely to behave with "good" biological global properties is to be rich in forcing structures. If genes really are usually nearly off or nearly full on, extended forcing structures seem likely to exist in cellular control circuits.

On the other hand, genes may be capable of finely graded levels of activity. Obtaining steady-state behavior in normal simple open chemical systems with reversible reactions does not require forcing structures. The extent to which cells achieve their global behaviors through such properties of some continuous dynamic systems is unclear. Perhaps the most reasonable guess at this point is that genes may rely on forcing structures to obtain homeostasis and other globally useful behavior, while the intermediate metabolic system may rely much more on nonextremal steady state behavior of its readily reversible reactions. (See Appendix 3 and Newman and Rice [30] for analyses of forcing structures in continuous systems.)

## 16. Conclusions and summary

The picture of a metazoan cell's genetic net which emerges is that of a system rich in forcible genes and with extensive forcing structures weaving through it rather like a reticulum, leaving pockets of nonforced genes functionally isolated from one another by the unalterable behavior of the forcing structures, once in their forced states. The forcible elements and forcing reticulum would provide the basic localization, and homeostasis in the behavior of the system. Different cell types would correspond to different patterns of activity, either steady state or cyclic, of the isolated, nonforced pockets.

We began by asking whether several global behaviors ubiquitously present in the gene control systems of organisms offered clues to the construction of those control systems by reflecting some basic ways genetic nets might most readily be built, or whether the ubiquitous characteristics were present as highly selective consequences of evolution. The building blocks of the genetic control circuitry are DNA, RNA, and protein. These molecules are particularly good at exhibiting high molecular specificity, thereby creating dynamic systems with few inputs per component, and rich in forcible elements and forcing structures. Just these systems almost automatically exhibit the ubiquitous properties mentioned: homeostasis, limited local reachability, a capacity to evolve while keeping old useful cell types, roughly the right number of cell types and right length periodicities, etc. Whether the model is right in detail, and it surely is not, it is nevertheless a real intimation that such a theory can be had, and that there is reason to hope for some common discoverable plan to the organization of genetic control systems.

## Appendix 1

### Theorems on forcing structures

1. DF. A binary element, $A$, receiving inputs from $K$ other elements, is forcible on a given input line $i$ if and only if, for one binary value on the $i$th input line, at time $T$, $A$ assumes the same binary value at $T + 1$, regardless of the binary values on the remaining $j \neq i$, $j = 1, 2, \cdots, K$ input lines at time $T$, i.e. for all $2^{K-1}$ combinations of the $j \neq i$ inputs, $A$ assumes the same value.

2. DF. The forced value of an element, $A$, is that binary value to which a forcing input can force $A$.

THEOREM 1. A. *An element $A$ having $K$ inputs can receive $0 \leq m \leq K$ forcing inputs.*

B. *The forced value of $A$ is identical for all $m > 1$.*

**Proof.** Consider the input matrix $K \times 2^K$ listing all states of the $K$ inputs to $A$.

For $A$ to be forcible on the $K$th input line, it is necessary and sufficient that for one value of the $K$th input line, say 1, element $A$ always assumes one binary value, say 0. The input matrix (IM) listing all states of the $K$ inputs has $2^K$ rows. Input $K$ takes on value 1 in $2^{K-1}$ rows, thus $2^{K-1}$ corresponding loci of the function column of $A$ must be filled with the forced value 0. The remaining $2^{K-1}$ loci may be filled in any manner and $A$ will be forcible by $K$.

Consider an input $j \neq K$. In the input matrix (IM) $j$ takes on both values 1 and 0 with respect to either single value of $K$; thus $j$ takes on both values opposite the $2^{K-1}$ loci in the function column of $A$ which have 0. Thus no single value of $j$ can force $A$ to a value different from 0. Therefore for any $j \neq i$, when $A$ is forcible on $i$ to value $x$, $j$ cannot force $A$ to $\bar{x}$. Conversely, $j$ too can force $A$ to $x$ (here $x = 0$). To achieve this, we note that in the $2^{K-1}$ loci of the function not yet filled, $1/4 = 2^{K-2}$ loci are places where $j \neq i$ $(i = K)$ takes on a single value, say 0, and $2^{K-2}$ are places where $j = 1$. Either set of $2^{K-2}$ additional loci of the function may be filled by additional forced values of $A$ (here 0). Successively, each of the remaining inputs may be made to force $A$. If $L$ inputs, $L \leq K$ are forcing, the $L + 1$ input has $2^{(K-L)}$ to fill with the forced value, 0. When $K$ inputs force, the final $K$th input can be made to force $K$, filling $2^{K-K} = 1$ remaining locus. This proves the theorem.

COROLLARY 1. *There are $2^{K+1}$ functions of $K$ inputs which force on all $K$ input lines.*

PROOF. To force on $K$ inputs, $(2^K - 1)$ loci of the $2^K$ loci in the function column must be filled with the same forced value. The last with the nonforced value (to exclude the functions tactology and contradiction which trivially force on all inputs). There are $2^K$ places where the single nonforcing value can be placed, and 2 choices of the forcing value, hence $2^{K+1}$ functions force on $K$ inputs.

THEOREM 2. *An upper bound on the number of boolean functions of inputs forcible on one or more input lines is:*

$$2^{K+1} \left[ 1 + \sum_{I=0}^{K-2} (2^{2^I} - 1) (K - I) \right] - 2K + 2.$$

**Proof.** We count by beginning with one of the $2^{K+1}$ boolean functions forcible on all $K$ input lines, and successively relax the number of input lines on which the function is forcible. Without loss of generality we choose the function forcible by all $K$ inputs when they are 0, which has 0 in every locus of the function except that corresponding to input state $(1111 \cdots 1)$. Let the order of the inputs be $A, B, C, D, \cdots, K$. We will relax the number of forcible inputs in this particular order, first relaxing forcing on $A$, but maintaining it on $B$, $C, \cdots, K$, etc.

To relax forcing on $A$, but maintain it on $B, C, \cdots, K$, we must alter the function by changing a 0 to a 1 at a locus of the function column corresponding to one or more input states where $A$ currently forces, but $B, C, \cdots, K$ do not. There is only one such state, $(011111 \cdots 1)$, hence only one way to relax forcing on this $K$th forcible input line.

To relax forcing on $B$, once $A$ is relaxed we must choose input states where $A$ is in either value, $B$ is in its forcing value, here 0, and $C, D, \cdots, K$ are in their nonforcing values, here 1. One or more of the corresponding loci of the function must be altered from 0 to 1. Such input states are $(x, 0, 111 \cdots 1)$, $x = 1$ or 0. There are $2^1 = 2$ such states, and $2^2 - 1$ ways of altering one or more corresponding loci of the function of 1.

If $I$ loci have already been relaxed from forcing, then

the input states of which one or more must be altered are $(x, x, x, x, 0, 111 \cdots 1)$, when the number of $x$ is $I$. Thus there are $2^I$ such states and $(2^{2^I} - 1)$ ways of altering one or more loci in the function to 1. When the first input, $A$, is being relaxed, none have yet been relaxed, thus $I = 0$, and $(2^{2^0} - 1) = 1$ ways to alter the function, as required. Since we want to count functions forcible on 1 or more input lines, $I$ should run from 0 to $K - 2$.

We now allow different orders of relaxing forcible input lines. When $I$ inputs have already been relaxed, there are $(K - I)$ input lines which are still forcible, hence $(K - I)$ choices of which input line next to relax. Thus the number of ways is $(2^{2^I} - 1)(K - I)$.

The sum is thus $1 + \sum_{I=0}^{K-2}(2^{2^I} - 1)(K - I)$ where the 1 is the initial function forcible on all $K$ input lines, and the sum term is an upper bound on the number of functions derivable from it which force on $K - 1$, $K - 2, \cdots, 1$ input lines. The sum is an upper bound since different permutations of order of relaxing forcing generate some identical functions.

There are $2^{K+1}$ initial functions forcible on all $K$ input lines, hence an upper bound on the number of functions of $K$ inputs forcible on 1 or more input lines is

$$2^{K+1} \left[ 1 + \sum_{I=0}^{K-2} (2^{2^I} - 1)(K - I) \right].$$

A slightly better upper bound is obtained by subtracting the $2K$ functions which only affirm or deny 1 input and have here each been counted 2 or more times and, adding tautology and contradiction which have not been counted, gives

$$2^{K=1} \left[ 1 + \sum_{I=0}^{K-2} (2^{2^I} - 1)(K - I) \right] - 2K + 2.$$

THEOREM 3. *An upper bound on the total number of forcible input lines among the $2^{2^K}$ functions of $K$ inputs is*

$$2^{K+1}\left[ K + \sum_{I=0}^{K-2} (2^{2^I} - 1)(K - I)(K - I - 1) \right].$$

**Proof.** In Theorem 2, the first 1 in the sum corresponds to the initial function forcible on $K$ input lines, hence it has $K$ forcing input lines. When $I$ input lines no longer force, we are counting the number which only force on $[K - (I + 1)]$ input lines $= (K - I - 1)$. The number of such functions is $(2^{2^I} - 1)(K - I)$. Multiplying yields the number of forcible input lines:

$$[(2^{2^I} - 1)(K - I)(K - I - 1)].$$

The $[- 2K + 2]$ in Theorem 2 becomes $[- 2K \circ 1 + 2K]$ $= 0$, for tautology and contradiciton are forcible, trivially, on all $K$ input lines.

THEOREM 4. *An upper bound on the expected number of forcible input lines, $R$, in a switching net of $N$ elements, each with $K$ inputs, where the boolean function assigned to each element is chosen at random among the $2^{2^K}$ possible functions of $K$ inputs is*

$$R < N \cdot$$

$$\left[ 2^{K+1}\left[ K + \sum_{I=0}^{K-2} (2^{2^I} - 1)(K - I)(K - I - 1) \right] \middle/ 2^{2^K} \right].$$

**Proof.** By Theorem 3 the numerator is an upper bound on the number of forcible input lines among the $2^{2^K}$ functions of $K$ inputs. Build a net with $2^{2^K}$ elements, assigning one function to each element, then the quotient inside the major brackets is the upper bound on the ratio of forcible input lines per element of the switching net. Multiplying by $N$ yields an upper bound on $R$.

This upper bound is a decreasing function of $K$ as $K$ increases, for $N$ constant.

THEOREM 5. *Let $R'$ be the (expected) actual number of forcing connections, not merely forcible input lines, in a net of $N$ elements*

$$R' < (NK/2) \cdot$$

$$\left[ 2^{K+1} \left[ K + \sum_{I=0}^{K-2} (2^{2^I} - 1)(K - I)(K - I - 1) \right] \Big/ 2^{2^K} \right]^2 .$$

**Proof.** The quantity inside the major bracket is the probability that one element $A$ is forcible on one or more input lines if its boolean function on $K$ inputs is randomly chosen. It will be *forced* if it not only has a forcible input line, but if the element $x$ which inputs to $A$ on that line is itself forcible, and if $x$'s forced value is the value which forces $A$. The latter probability is $\frac{1}{2}$. The former probability is itself the expression in the major bracket. But $A$ can have up to $K$ forcible input lines. Hence the upper bound on the actual forcing connections is the expression in the major brackets squared, multiplied by $K/2$.

This upper bound decreases for $K > 2$; $K = 2$, $R' = 4N$; $K = 3$, $R' \approx \frac{1}{2}N$; $K = 4$, $R' = 2^{-9}N$.

THEOREM 6. *A lower bound on the number of functions of $K$ inputs forcible on 1 or more input lines is $2 \cdot 2^{2^{(K-1)}}$.*

**Proof.** With $K$ inputs, the input matrix is $2^K$ long. Let the $i$th input force to the value 1, then $2^{K-1}$ loci of the function column are specified, $2^{K-1}$ are left which may be filled many ways with 1 and 0.

There are $2^{2^{(K-1)}}$ ways of doing this. But we might initially have chosen to let $i$ force the function to 0, thus there are $2 \cdot 2^{2^{K-1}}$ ways for at least $i$ to force. This procedure counts the function which has *only* $i$ as an input twice. However it is a lower bound by considerably more than 2, since each of the $K$ inputs might have been chosen initially, and many ways each can force are not counted.

COROLLARY. *A lower bound on the number of forcible input lines in a net of N elements is*

$$R > \frac{N(2 \cdot 2^{2^{(K-1)}})}{2^{2^K}} = \frac{N2 \cdot 2^{(2^K)/2}}{2^{2^K}},$$

*which decreases as* $K \to N$, *N fixed.*

**Proof.** As above in Theorem 3.

THEOREM 7. *The number of forcing inputs R in a net of N elements receiving K inputs each, with randomly chosen boolean functions, is a decreasing function of* $K > 2$, *as K increases.*

**Proof.** At $K = 2$, the lower bound of $R$ is $\frac{1}{2}$. By $K = 4$, the upper bound is $1/32$, and decreases for increasing $K$.

### Appendix 2

#### The size and number of forcing loops

Let $N$ be the number of elements in a switching net, and $R$ be the number of forcing connections among the $N$.

Consider a forcing loop length $j \ll N$. The number of ways of choosing $j$ elements, all different, is

$$N!/j!(N-j)!.$$

For each set of $j$, the number of different directed forcing loops is $j!/j = (j-1)!$.

Thus the number of different directed loops of length $j$, all different, is

$$\frac{N!}{j!(N-j)!} \cdot (j-1)! = \frac{N!}{j(N-j)!} \approx \frac{N^j}{j},$$

for $j \ll N$.

For any particular pair of elements, the probability that there is an arrow between them, oriented in a particular way, is $R/2N^2$, where self-connection is allowed.

The chance that all $j$ are connected into a directed forcing loop, granted that arrows occur between each successive pair 1, 2; 2, 3; $\cdots$, $j$, 1, is $(2^{-j}) \cdot 2$, since two-directed orientation works.

Hence the chance that a $j$ loop is a directed forcing loop is

$$2^{-j} \cdot 2 \left( \frac{R}{2N^2} \right)^j = 2 \left( \frac{R}{N^2} \right)^j.$$

The expected number of forcing loops length $j \ll N$ is

$$\frac{N^j}{j} \cdot 2 \left( \frac{R}{N^2} \right)^j = \frac{2}{j} \cdot \left( \frac{R}{N} \right)^j.$$

The expected number of elements on forcing loops length $j$ is

$$j \cdot \frac{2}{j} \left( \frac{R}{N} \right)^j = 2 \left( \frac{R}{N} \right)^j = 2\alpha^j,$$

where $\alpha = R/N$.

Hence the expected number of points on forcing loops is

$$2(\alpha + \alpha^2 + \alpha^3 + \alpha^4 + \alpha^N) \approx \frac{2\alpha}{1 - \alpha} \text{ (for } N \text{ large)} = \frac{2R}{N - R}.$$

Each point sends arrows to an expected $R/N = \alpha$ other points.

The total "progeny" in a stochastic process where the expected immediate progeny is $\mu$ is $1/1 - \mu$. Hence the total number of elements in a given loop element's descendent forcing tree is $1/1 - \alpha$, $\alpha = R/N$. An upper bound on the expected number of elements either on forcing loops or descendent from them is

$$\frac{2\alpha}{1 - \alpha} \cdot \frac{1}{1 - \alpha} = \frac{2\alpha}{1 - 2\alpha + \alpha^2} = \frac{2NR}{N^2 - NR + R^2}.$$

These calculations require $R < N$.

## Appendix 3

In view of the intractability of systems with many components coupled by strongly nonlinear equations, establishing the character of possible mappings from the behavior of binary switching nets to "homologous" continuous systems might be expected to be helpful. Insight gained from switching systems might be applied to continuous systems. In Glass and Kauffman, 1971,[4] we discuss briefly the similarity of state cycles of switching nets and of cyclic sequences of states of homologous continuous systems, where a state is the current sign of each component's first derivative, and thus a binary state.

If boolean addition of clusters of adjacent states of the continuous net's cyclic sequence of binary states is performed, it has been possible in several instances to find clusterings, preserving the initial ordering of the continuous net's state cycle, which provide a 1:1 map from continuous to switching systems. This suggests that the number and kind of cyclic behavior of appropriate continuous systems parallels that of homologous switching nets.

The concept of a forcing structure may be generalized to continuous systems. If a binary element is forcible on an input line, then *one* binary value on that line puts the element in *one* value, on or off, regardless of the values on the remaining input lines. A reasonable generalization to continuous systems is that if a continuous element is forcible on a continuous input line, then one direction of change of that input level constrains the element to be above (or below) its level prior to the input change, regardless of the behavior of the other inputs. We may then define the relation of forcing be-

---

tween two elements as before. An element $i$ forces an element $j$, if $i$ is forcible on an input line, if $j$ is forcible on an input from $i$, and if the direction of change in which $i$ is forcible is the direction which forces $i$ to change in its forced direction.

For convenience, we normalize the maximum level of activity of a component at 1, and minimum at 0. Then each element realizes a function on its $K$ inputs which can be put in a $K + 1$ dimensional hypercube. Consider a 3-dimensional cube representing an element $Z$'s functions on its $x$ and $y$ inputs. Suppose the function is 0 if $x$ or $y$ is 0, and 1 if $x$ or $y$ or both are 1. The extreme values are the OR function. Project the *minimum* of the function surface on to the $zx$ plane. If the projection is monotonic, increasing from 0 to 1 as $x$ increases from 0 to 1, then $z$ is forcible on its input line from $x$. If the $zy$ projection is also monotonic, $z$ is forcible on its $y$ input. In both cases it is forcible in only one direction, up, for we have considered the projection of the minimum of the function surface.

Similarly consider a function which takes extremal values 0, 0, 0, 1 for $x = y = 0$, $x = 1$ $y = 0$, $x = 0$ $y = 1$, $x = y = 1$, i.e. at the extremes of an AND function. Consider the projection of the *maximum* of the function surface onto the $xz$ and $yz$ planes. If either is monotonic, that input line is forcible in the down direction by decreasing levels of the input.

As in switching nets, if an element is forcible up on one input line, it may be forcible up on other input lines, but cannot be forcible down on any input lines; for the *minimum* of the function surface cannot be monotonic up in one projection $xz$, as $x$ goes from 0 to 1 and simultaneously the *maximum* of the function surface monotonic down on another projection, $yz$, as $y$ goes from 0 to 1.

We may define forcing gain. If the projection of the minimum of a function onto the $xz$ plane is not only monotonic up, but is above the main diagonal of the cube extending from (00) to (11) on the $xz$ plane, then in that region where the minimum is above the main diagonal, the forcible input has positive gain. Similarly, if the projection of the maximum both monotonic down, and in some region of $x$, below the main diagonal extending from 01 to 10 in the $xz$ plane, then the input $x$ has positive gain forcing down.

By the definition of "forcing" between continuous elements, extended forcing structures may be built.

Consider a forcing loop with gain over the entire domain of each forcing input. Over time, each element will be driven to its maximal forced value, and so will any down stream forcing tree with gain.

Around a forcing loop, or along a descendent forcing tree, some elements may have positive gain, others negative gain. If net gain around a loop is positive all elements will be forced to extremal values, and so also the loop's descendent forcing tree. If net gain is positive along any section of an acyclic forcing structure, later elements will tend to be at more extremal values.

We note that elements whose activity follows simple Michaelas Menton type kinetic curves on control input levels would be capable of such gain, for their response curves will be above the main diagonals if facilitated by a control input, and below if inhibited.

Components realizing sigmoid responses on inputs can show positive gain in the neighborhood of their extremal forced value, and can therefore be linked into extended forcing structures whose extremal forced values state can be stable.

It is a necessary, but not sufficient, condition for a continuous function of $K$ inputs to be forcible on one or more input lines that the homologous boolean function obtained by considering the values of the function at the corners of the canonical function hypercube be itself a forcible boolean function. Since the density of forcible boolean functions is greatest at $K = 2$ and decreases as $K$ increases, the density of appropriately monotonic continuous functions must also decrease as $K$ increases. Extensive continuous forcing structures would be unlikely when $K$ is large, and more likely for small numbers of continuous inputs.

In summary, it appears that the concept of a forcing structure can be generalized to continuous components. Such structures would offer powerful constraints on the dynamic behavior of large systems. The extent to which continuous dynamic systems oscillate in ways homologous to appropriate switching systems remains a subject worth intensive study. Further, the extent to which continuous systems whose components, like genes, realize reactions which are nearly irreversible on the time scale of the forward reaction, and strongly sigmoid in response to control inputs, can show constrained homeostatic behavior and other "good" global behaviors without being rich in forcing structures remains to be elucidated.

Newman and Rice [30] have given a somewhat similar discussion of the implications of monotonicity in continuous dynamic systems.

**Acknowledgement.** The author wishes to thank Drs. John Maynard Smith, Stuart Newman and Leon Glass for many helpful discussions. He is particularly grateful to the Department of Biology, University of Cincinnati, for their generous offer of computer time. This research was supported in part by the Sloan Foundation.

Corollary 1, Appendix 1, was first proved by Newman and Rice [30] in 1971. Several steps in the analysis in Appendix 2 are due to John Maynard Smith.

## References

1. V. G. Allfrey, *In regulatory mechanisms for protein synthesis in mammalian cells*, San Pietro, Lamborg and Kenney (editors), Academic Press, New York, 1968.

2. M. Ashburner, P. C. 1970.

3. _____, Chromosoma **27** (1969), 47.

4. _____, Chromosoma **27** (1969), 156.

5. _____, *Chromosomes today*. Vol. 2, edited by C. D. Darlington and K. R. Lewis, Oliver & Boyd, Edinburgh, 1969.

6. H. Berendes, Chromosoma **22** (1967), 274.

7. _____, Chromosoma **24** (1968), 418.

8. J. A. Boezi and D. B. Cowie, Biophys. J. 1 (1961), 639.

9. J. Bonner and R. C. Huang, Proc. Nat. Acad. Sci. U. S. A. **48** (1967), 1216.

10. S. Bourgeois, *Thesis*, Faculté de Sciences, University of Paris, 1966.

11. R. J. Britten and E. H. Davidson, Science **165** (1969), 349.

12. U. Clever, Ann. Zool. 7 (1966), 33.

13. G. N. Cohen, *The regulation of cell metabolism*, Hermann, Paris; Holt, Rinehart and Winston, New York, 1968.

14. P. Erdös and A. Rényi, *On random graphs*. I, Publ. Math. Debrecen 6 (1959), 290-297. MR **22** # 10924.

15. _____, *On the evolution of random graphs*, Magyar Tud. Akad. Mat. Kutató Int. Közl. **5** (1960), 17-61. MR **23** # A2338.

16. A. S. Fraser, *Towards a theoretical biology*. Vol. 3, C. H. Waddington (editor), Aldine, Chicago, Ill., 1970, p. 56.

17. W. Gehring, *The stability of the differentiated state*, H. Ursprung (editor), Springer-Verlag, New York, 1968, p. 136.

18. W. Gilbert and Hill B. Muller, Proc. Nat. Acad. Sci. U. S. A. **56** (1966), 1891.

19. _____, Proc. Nat. Acad. Sci. U. S. A. **58** (1967), 2415.

20. E. Hadorn, *Major problems in developmental biology*, E. J. M. Locke (editor), Academic Press, New York, 1967.

21. L. A. Herzenberg, Biochim. Biophys. Acta. **31** (1959), 525.

22. F. Jacob and J. Monod, Cold Spring Harbor Sympos. Quantitative Biology, vol. 22, 1961, p. 193.

23. _____, Twenty-First Sympos. of the Society for the Study of Development and Growth, M. Locke (editor), Academic Press, New York, 1963, p. 30.

24. S. M. S. Kauffman, (in preparation).

25. S. Kauffman, J. Theoret. Biol. **22** (1969), 437.

26. _____, *Current topics in developmental biology*. Vol. 6, A. Monroy and A. Moscona (editors), Academic Press, New York (to appear).

27. _____, Nature **224** (1969), 177-178.

28. _____, J. Cybernetics 1 (1971), 71-96.

**29.** J. Monod, J. Changeaux and J. P. Wyman, J. Mol. Biol. **88** (1965), 12.

**30.** S. Newman and S. Rice, Proc. Nat. Acad. Sci. U. S. A. **68** (1971), 92-96.

**31.** M. Ptashne, Proc. Nat. Acad. Sci. U. S. A. **57** (1967), 306.

**32.** ———, Nature **214** (1967), 232.

**33.** J. M. Rendel, *Canalization and gene control*, Logos Press, London, 1967.

**34.** A. D. Riggs, et al., J. Mol. Biol. **51** (1970), 303.

**35.** T. K. Shires, S. Kauffman and H. Pitot, "The membron. A functional hypothesis for the translational regulation of genetic expression," in *Biomembranes*. Vol. 2, Marcel Dekker, (to appear).

**36.** G. Tomkins, "Regulatory mechanism for protein synthesis," in *Mammalian cells*, Anthony San Pietro (editor), Academic Press, New York and London, 1968.

**37.** C. H. Waddington, *New patterns in genetics and development*, Columbia Univ. Press, New York, 1962.

**38.** C. Walker and W. R. Ashby, Kybernetics **3** (1965), 100.

**39.** C. Walters, et al., J. Theoret. Biol. **15** (1967), 208.

# AUTHOR INDEX

Roman numbers refer to pages on which a reference is made to a work of an author.

*Italic numbers* refer to pages on which a complete reference to a work by an author is given.

**Boldface numbers** indicate the first page of an article in this volume.

# SUBJECT INDEX

DATE DUE